A & P I

Course Workbook

Second Edition

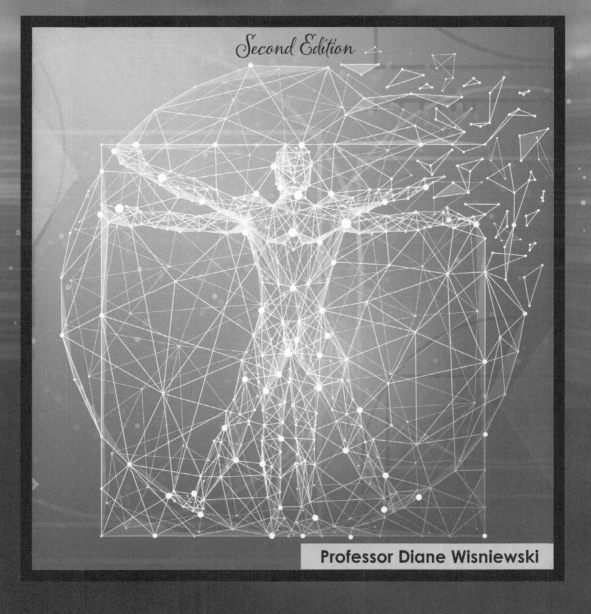

Professor Diane Wisniewski

Kendall Hunt
publishing company

Cover image © Shutterstock.com

www.kendallhunt.com
Send all inquiries to:
4050 Westmark Drive
Dubuque, IA 52004-1840

Copyright © 2018, 2019 by Kendall Hunt Publishing Company

ISBN: 978-1-5249-8691-9

Published in the United States of America

CONTENTS

UNIT 5

UNIT 6

UNIT 1

Chapters 1-3 Lab

Introduction to the Human Body, Chemistry and Biochemistry, and Cells

INTRODUCTION TO THE HUMAN BODY

LAB ACTIVITY: Metric Measurement

The metric system is used for measurement in science and medicine. Fill in the blanks in each of the following:

The base unit for length is _____.

The base unit for volume is _____.

The base unit for weight is _____.

The prefix *kilo-* means _____.

The prefix *centi-* means _____.

The prefix *milli-* means _____.

The prefix *micro-* means _____.

Temperature in the metric system (Answer the following using Celsius.)

Water boils at _____ degrees and water freezes at _____ degrees.

Average body temperature is _____.

Measure and record the following making sure to identify the units of measure after your answer.

1. Using the meter sticks, choose an object at your table and fill in the following.

    Centimeters: _____x_____

    Millimeters: _____x_____

    Area: _____ in centimeters^2

    Area: _____ in millimeters^2

2. Next, calculate the volume in cubic centimeters (cm^3).

    _____cm^3

3. What is the mass of the object?

    Grams: _____

    Milligrams: _____

4. Calculate the density of the object.

    Mass/Volume = _____

Use a graduated cylinder and measure out the following volumes. Check it off once you have completed the task.

5. What is the relationship between 1 mL and 1 cm^3?

    _____

Volume	✓
1 mL	
10 mL	
100 mL	

THE BODY SYSTEMS

Body System:	Major Function(s):	Major Organs:
Integumentary System		
Skeletal System		
Articular System (the joints of the body)		
Muscular System		
Nervous System		
Sensory System		
Endocrine System		
Cardiovascular System		
Lymphatic System		

THE BODY SYSTEMS, (CONT.)

Body System:	Major Function(s):	Major Organs:
Respiratory System		
Digestive System		
Urinary System		
Reproductive System		

Working with your lab partners, demonstrate and/or find the location of the following anatomical terms. Check off as you complete them.

Term	✔	Term	✔
anatomical position		superior	
right side		inferior	
left side		proximal	
supine		distal	
prone		lateral	
anterior		medial	
posterior		superficial	
thoracic		deep	
cervical		lumbar	

Name the abdominopelvic quadrant AND abdominopelvic region for each organ. Some may occupy more than one region/quadrant. If so, make sure you write all quadrants.

Organ:	Quadrant(s):	Region:
stomach		
appendix		
spleen		
liver (majority)		
urinary bladder		
belly button (umbilicus)		
pancreas		
rectum		

LAB: Use the torso model to identify the following body planes, cavities, and membranes. Check off as you complete them.

Planes	✔	Cavities	✔
frontal/coronal		thoracic	
sagittal		abdominal	
midsagittal		pelvic	
transverse		pleura	
peritoneum		pericardium	

Match each term in column A with its description in column B.

Column A   Column B

A. subatomic particles   _____ 1. this type of study requires magnification to view
B. molecule   _____ 2. protection from environment; includes skin, hair, nails
C. cell   _____ 3. study of the body's functions
D. tissue   _____ 4. responsible for transporting materials throughout the body
E. organ   _____ 5. enhancement of a stimulus—moves the body away from homeostasis
F. organ system   _____ 6. this type of anatomy can be seen with the naked eye
G. integumentary system   _____ 7. defense against infection
H. muscular system   _____ 8. the term for a stable internal environment
I. endocrine system   _____ 9. support and protection of internal structures, blood cell production
J. cardiovascular system _____ 10. movement and heat production
K. respiratory system   _____ 11. protons, neutrons, electrons
L. urinary system   _____ 12. two or more tissues combined for several functions
M. reproductive system   _____ 13. processing of food
N. skeletal system   _____ 14. adjusting activities in response to change (to keep homeostasis)
O. nervous system   _____ 15. a group of cells performing a specific function
P. lymphatic system   _____ 16. produces hormones
Q. anatomy   _____ 17. two or more atoms bonded together
R. digestive system   _____ 18. two or more organs combined for general function
S. homeostasis   _____ 19. elimination of wastes by filtering the blood
T. microscopic anatomy   _____ 20. brings the body back into normal range (homeostasis)
U. negative feedback   _____ 21. smallest whole unit of biological organization
V. set point   _____ 22. the control center of the body
W. positive feedback   _____ 23. delivery of air for gas exchange
X. regulation   _____ 24. desired value in a homeostatic environment
Y. macroscopic anatomy   _____ 25. production of sex cells
Z. physiology   _____ 26. study of the body's structures

Three parts of a homeostatic regulatory mechanism: _____

Negative Feedback: _____

Positive Feedback: _____

CHEMISTRY AND BIOCHEMISTRY

CHEMISTRY TERMS CROSSWORD PUZZLE

Across

2. these compounds stabilize pH
4. two or more atoms bonded together
5. a type of suspension such as Jell-O with fruit cocktail in it
8. proteins that start chemical reactions
12. a type of molecule also known as sugar
13. a type of molecule also known as fat

Down

1. a combination of two or more substances not chemically bonded
3. the liquid in which substances are dissolved
5. two or more different atoms bonded together
6. the basic structural unit of nucleic acids such as DNA
7. the smallest unit of matter
9. the substance that is dissolved in a solution
10. these consist of long chains of amino acids
11. a type of compound that contains hydrogen and oxygen
14. a type of stored energy

COMPOUNDS, ELEMENTS, MOLES, AND MOLECULES ACTIVITY

PART I

Using the different groups of material you have been given, along with the Periodic Table, determine the answers to each of the following sections.

Determine which color represents each of the following:

Element:	Bead Color:
carbon	
oxygen	
nitrogen	
hydrogen	
sodium	
chlorine	

Now, tell why you believe this to be true:

_____

_____

PART II

The following is the start of a diagram of a carbon atom and that of a sodium atom. Determine which of the following should be carbon and which should be sodium (use logic here ☺) and draw, in the correct place, the correct number of protons, electrons, and neutrons.

Use + to represent protons
Use – to represent electrons
Use *n* to represent neutrons

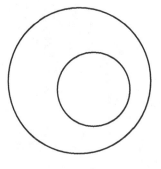

Atom type: _____

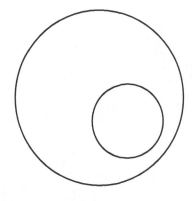

Atom type: _____

DO NOT OPEN ANY SAMPLE TUBES EXCEPT FOR E and F – *During Part IV.*

PART III

Using the Periodic Table of the elements and the samples you have been given (A–D), determine the answers to the following questions.

Samples A–D

1. Does *Sample A* represent an element or a compound? *Hint: Look very carefully at each atom before you answer.*

    _____

    How do you know? _____

2. You have 1 mole of *Sample B*. Using the Periodic Table and the given weight, determine its identity.

    _____

3. Does *Sample C* represent an element or a compound? _____

    How do you know? _____

    Do you know anything else about it? _____

4. Suppose *Sample D* is 1 mole of He (helium). How much does it weigh? _____

    How many atoms are present? _____

    What if it were 1 mole of Au (gold)? How much would it weigh? _____

    How many atoms would be present? _____

PART IV (SAMPLES E AND F)

Using the felt as your work surface, and one sample at a time, separate the atoms by type. Use the data chart and hints provided to determine the answers to each question.

Hints: When writing a chemical formula, it is usually C (carbon), followed by H (hydrogen), N (nitrogen), and O (oxygen). If you have sodium (Na) in your sample, write that symbol first. If you have F (fluorine) in your sample, follow the above rule, but place it after H (hydrogen). The number of atoms present is written after the chemical symbol in subscript. For example, the formula for water is H_2O.

<u>Sample E:</u>

1. What is the chemical formula of **Sample E**?

   _____

Sample identity? _____

2. Is this a compound, molecule, or both?

   _____

   How many total atoms are present? _____

<u>Sample F:</u>

1. What is the chemical formula of **Sample F**?

   _____

Sample identity? _____

2. Is this a compound, molecule, or both?

   _____

   How many total atoms are present?

   _____

Data Chart:

Element:	Color:
H (hydrogen)	green
C (carbon)	blue
N (nitrogen)	yellow
O (oxygen)	white
F (fluorine)	pink
Na (sodium)	brown

Hints to help you identify your samples:

Group #:	Sample E Hints:
Group 1	Used as an antiseptic and can lighten hair
Group 2	A strong base used for household cleaning
Group 3	Worldwide, 2 billion pounds are produced; Europeans (and the Easter Bunny) are the largest consumers of this
Group 4	Can be used to relieve heartburn or for baking chocolate chip cookies
Group 5	Helps get you going in the morning
Group 6	Prevents scurvy
Group 7	Was first formulated as a surgical antiseptic
Group 8	Also known as acetylsalicylic acid
Group #:	**Sample F Hints:**
Group 1	Until 1903, this was an important ingredient in Coca Cola
Group 2	In Amsterdam, you can go to a counter (much like at a deli) and order this
Group 3	Afghanistan produces 87% of the world's supply of this
Group 4	It is estimated that 70 million people take this medication each year; it is available over the counter and by prescription
Group 5	24.4 million prescriptions are filled for this every year in the United States
Group 6	Makes dental work a lot "funnier"
Group 7	Extracted from the Iranian poppy and is legal in many countries (not the United States, though)
Group 8	The main ingredient in teething gel

Place the following in the correct order from smallest to largest.

_____ diatomic molecule   _____ proton   _____ polyatomic molecule

_____ atom   _____ chemical compound

Match each term in column A with its description in column B.

Column A
A. atom
B. element
C. compound
D. ion
E. glucose
F. covalent bond
G. decomposition
H. lipid
I. ionic bond
J. synthesis
K. pH
L. phospholipid bilayer
M. organic
N. triglyceride
O. solution
P. DNA
Q. enzyme
R. electrolytes
S. protein
T. Periodic Table

Column B
_____ 1. the simplest form of sugar
_____ 2. a chemical reaction that breaks large molecules into smaller ones
_____ 3. the main component of natural fats, also a type of fat in the blood
_____ 4. Na, Cl, K, Mg, and Ca are examples; it conducts electricity in solution
_____ 5. the smallest unit of matter
_____ 6. cannot be broken down physically; in Periodic Table
_____ 7. the description of the composition of the cell membrane
_____ 8. a chemical reaction of making small molecules into large ones
_____ 9. makes up the structural components of the body
_____ 10. is living or once was (has carbon)
_____ 11. the mixture of a solute in a solvent
_____ 12. a substance known as a fat
_____ 13. controls/speeds up reaction rates
_____ 14. this type of bond shares electrons
_____ 15. this type of bond transfers electrons between atoms
_____ 16. two or more different atoms bonded together
_____ 17. a chart that arranges elements based on atomic number
_____ 18. a measurement of how acidic or alkaline something is
_____ 19. the term for any atom with an electrical charge
_____ 20. this is what determines our inherited characteristics

Complete the following questions.

1. Table salt has the chemical formula NaCl. What type of bond would cause these two atoms to form a crystal when they bond together?

2. Digestion involves breaking down food into molecules that can be absorbed. What type of reaction is this?

3. *"The minimum amount of energy necessary for a chemical reaction to begin"* is a description of what term?

4. About how long can a person live without ingesting any water?

5. If you are sweating excessively while you are exercising or working, you might drink an electrolyte solution like PowerAde or Gatorade. Why is this helpful?

6. What is range of the pH scale? What is the neutral value, what is the acid value, and what is the base value on the scale?

7. In a beaker of sugar and water, identify the solution, the solute, and the solvent.

   Solution _____

   Solute _____

   Solvent _____

pH LAB – Answer the following questions.

Mathematically pH = -log H⁺. Log, or logarithm, is an exponent. The log (exponent) of 10^{-3} is -3.

1. The log of 10^{-7} is _____. If $H^+ = 10^{-4}$, the pH = -log H^+ = -(-4) = _____.

Therefore, pH is the negative log of H^+.

2. If $H^+ = 10^{-12}$, then the pH = _____. If $H^+ = 10^{-1}$, then the pH = _____.

An acid is a solution that can be defined in terms of a number called the _pH_ of that solution. The pH scale is a measurement of the concentration of hydrogen ions (and hydroxide ions) in solution.

The pH range is from 0 to 14, with a pH of 7 indicating a _neutral_ solution. A pH of below 7 indicates an _acid_ solution. A pH of greater than 7 indicates a _basic_ solution. Answer each of the following:

3. A pH of 3 indicates a(n) _____ solution.

4. A pH of 7 indicates a(n) _____ solution.

5. A pH of 9 indicates a(n) _____ solution.

Water is very slightly ionized. $H_2O \rightarrow H^+ + OH^-$. Hydrogen ion concentration (H^+) in water is 10^{-7}.

6. What is the pH of water? _____ Is water acidic, basic, or neutral? _____

7. Check which of the following pH values indicates a solution containing a strong acid?

_____ 6   _____ 7   _____ 1   _____ 10   _____ 12

8. Urine has a pH range of 5.5 to 6.9, so it is a _____ solution.

   a) Weak acid   b) Strong acid   c) Neutral   d) Weak base   e) Strong base

9. The juices in the stomach have a pH range 1.6 to 1.8, so they make up a _____ solution.

   a) Weak acid   b) Strong acid   c) Neutral   d) Weak base   e) Strong base

A difference of 1 in pH is equivalent to a 10-fold difference in acid or base strength. That is, an acid of pH 2 is 10 times stronger than an acid of pH 3. Likewise, a base of pH 10 is 100 times stronger than a base of pH 8.

10. A solution of pH 4.73 is _____ times stronger than one of pH 5.73.

11. A solution of pH 9.81 is 10 times as _____ (weak/strong) as one of pH 10.81.

Recall that acids give off hydrogen ions (H⁺) or protons in solution. Both hydrochloric acid (HCl) and acetic acid (CH₃COOH) are acids, as indicated by the following reactions.

$$HCl \rightarrow H^+ + Cl^-$$ $$CH_3COOH \Leftrightarrow CH_3COO^- + H^+$$

12. Sulfuric acid (H_2SO_4) yields relatively many H^+ ions in solution. It is a _____ (strong/weak) acid.

13. Citric acid, which yields relatively few H^+ ions in solution, is a _____ (strong/weak) acid.

A base accepts or reacts with protons (hydrogen ions).

14. A strong base reacts with relatively _____ (many/few) H^+ ions.

15. A weak base reacts with relatively _____ (many/few) H^+ ions.

A buffer solution is one that maintains a constant pH upon the addition of small amounts of either acid or base. A buffer consists of a weak acid and a weak base. A buffer solution can "mop up" excess H^+ if added to a solution, or it can release H^+ if the H^+ concentration drops.

16. What effect should removal of acid (which is equivalent in effect to the addition of base) have on the pH of a buffer system? In other words, describe what the buffers would do to the solution.

The pH of the blood (a buffer solution) lies in the range 7.35 to 7.45.

17. Normal metabolic processes (from muscle activity) will add acid to the bloodstream. Blood has buffers in it. Describe what the buffers would do.

pH TESTING

To test the pH of a solution, you will use a test strip for all solutions, **except for the bleach**. You will use a pH meter for this one. Record each solution's pH in this table.

Test Substance	pH	Acid, Base, or Neutral?

LAB: LIVER ENZYME LAB

Background Information

<u>Catalase</u> (the suffix -*ase* indicates an enzyme) is the enzyme found in liver. <u>Catalase</u> decomposes poisonous hydrogen peroxide in tissues into water and oxygen. The chemical reaction is written like this:

$$2 H_2O_2 \rightarrow 2H_2O + O$$

hydrogen peroxide → water + oxygen

PRELAB QUESTIONS

Complete the following questions before you start this activity.

1. What is activation energy?

2. What is a catalyst?

3. What is an enzyme?

4. What is a decomposition reaction?

5. What does the term *substrate* mean?

PROCEDURE:
1. Label four test tubes A, B, C, and control.
2. Add hydrogen peroxide (H_2O_2) to each of the four test tubes to 1 cm in depth.
3. To the control test tube, do not add anything else. Just set this tube in the test tube rack.
4. Use scissors to snip the liver samples into pieces about the size of a green pea.
5. To test Tube A, add a piece of *raw* liver about the size of a pea.
6. To test Tube B, add a piece of *cooked* liver about the size of a pea.
7. To test Tube C, add a piece of liver treated with hydrochloric acid (*HCl*).
8. Wait 15 to 20 minutes. Record the height of the foam in centimeters in each tube.
9. Complete the data table.

DATA TABLE

Tube Identification	Contents of the Tube (fill this in)	Height of Foam (in cm)
Control	H_2O_2	
A		
B		
C		

ANALYSIS

1. Which test tube showed the best results (in terms of height of the foam)? Why?

2. What is the substrate in this experiment?

3. What is the enzyme in this experiment?

4. What happened when you used cooked liver? Why do you think you got those results?

5. What happened when you used liver treated with an acid? Why do you think you got this result?

6. What is meant by the term *denatured*? What does it have to do with an *active site* of an enzyme?

CELLS

Match each term in column A with its description in column B.

Column A   Column B

A. cytoplasm   _____ 1. organelle used for packaging of proteins
B. organelles   _____ 2. organelle used to destroy cellular debris and clean it up
C. cell membrane   _____ 3. organelle used to detoxify hydrogen peroxide
D. nucleus   _____ 4. made up of amino acids; component of muscle, for example
E. rough E.R.   _____ 5. extension of cell membrane used to increase area
F. smooth E.R.   _____ 6. "brain" of the cell; contains chromosomes
G. ribosome   _____ 7. tiny "organs" in the cytoplasm
H. lysosome   _____ 8. movement of water molecules from high to low concentration
I. peroxisome   _____ 9. contains DNA and genetics
J. mitochondria   _____ 10. contains the base uracil; used for protein synthesis
K. centrioles   _____ 11. specific site of protein synthesis
L. microvilli   _____ 12. fluid portion of the cell
M. mitosis   _____ 13. movement of molecules from high to low concentration
N. meiosis   _____ 14. cell division in a sex cell
O. osmosis   _____ 15. organelle used for making hormones and lipids
P. diffusion   _____ 16. deoxyribonucleic acid
Q. chromosome   _____ 17. cell division of a body cell
R. protein   _____ 18. outer boundary of the cell
S. DNA   _____ 19. organelles used during mitosis; develops the spindle fibers
T. RNA   _____ 20. makes energy for the cell; the "powerhouse" of the cell
U. cilia   _____ 21. "hairy" extensions on the cell membrane

Complete the following questions.

1. Explain the difference between extracellular fluid and intracellular fluid.

2. What is the abbreviation for extracellular fluid? For intracellular fluid? Which is most abundant in the body?

3. What is meant by the term "concentration gradient"?

Match each transport process in column A with its definition in column B.

Column A   Column B

A. diffusion   _____ movement of molecules from inside a cell to the outside of a cell

B. osmosis   _____ the process of separating suspended solid matter from a liquid

C. active transport   _____ movement of molecules to an area of high concentration using cellular
                                energy

D. endocytosis   _____ movement of molecules from an area of high concentration to low
                                concentration

E. exocytosis   _____ movement of molecules from outside of a cell to inside of a cell

F. filtration   _____ movement of water from an area of high concentration to low
                                concentration

4. Why would a liver cell need a lot of smooth E.R. in the cytoplasm?

5. Why would a pancreas cell need a lot of rough E.R. and ribosomes in the cytoplasm?

6. What does *water-soluble* mean?

7. What does *lipid-soluble* mean?

8. Identify whether each of the following scenarios will cause the RBCs to swell, shrink, or remain the
   same.

Isotonic

Hypotonic

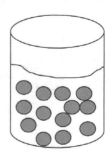
Hypertonic

_____   _____   _____

9. What is transcription?

10. What is translation?

11. Provide the mRNA sequence and the amino acid sequence from the following DNA strand:

DNA: T A C A T G G A T G A T C G A T C G A C T

mRNA:

SECOND LETTER									
		A		U		C		G	
A	AAA	Lysine	AUA	Isoleucine	ACA	Threonine	AGA	Arginine	A
	AAU	Aspargine	AUU	Isoleucine	ACU	Threonine	AGU	Serine	U
	AAC	Aspargine	AUC	Isoleucine	ACC	Threonine	AGC	Serine	C
	AAG	Lysine	AUG	INITIATION CODON Methionine	ACG	Threonine	AGG	Arginine	G
U	UAA	STOP CODON	UUA	Leucine	UCA	Serine	UGA	STOP CODON	A
	UAU	Tyrosine	UUU	Phenylalanine	UCU	Serine	UGU	Cysteine	U
	UAC	Tyrosine	UUC	Phenylalanine	UCC	Serine	UGC	Cysteine	C
	UAG	STOP CODON	UUG	Leucine	UCG	Serine	UGG	Tryptophan	G
C	CAA	Glutamine	CUA	Leucine	CCA	Proline	CGA	Arginine	A
	CAU	Histidine	CUU	Leucine	CCU	Proline	CGU	Arginine	U
	CAC	Histidine	CUC	Leucine	CCC	Proline	CGC	Arginine	C
	CAG	Glutamine	CUG	Leucine	CCG	Proline	CGG	Arginine	G
G	GAA	Glutamic acid	GUA	Valine	GCA	Alanine	GGA	Glycine	A
	GAU	Aspartic acid	GUU	Valine	GCU	Alanine	GGU	Glycine	U
	GAC	Aspartic Acid	GUC	Valine	GCC	Alanine	GGC	Glycine	C

FIRST LETTER (left side) — *THIRD LETTER* (right side)

Using this chart, list the amino acid sequence from the mRNA code in #10.

12. Name the three types of RNA.

13. List a few reasons *why* a cell would need to divide.

14. What is happening in interphase of the cell cycle?

15. List the four phases of mitosis in their correct order.

16. What would happen if a cell cannot stop dividing? That is, what would we call this?

17. Give an example of a type of cell and/or tissue that would be described by the following:

   a. Always divide _____

   b. Sometimes divide _____

   c. Never divides after development _____

KARYOTYPE ACTIVITY

A *karyotype* is the sorting of chromosomes. Chromosomes are sorted by size, number, and arrangement within the nucleus. A karyotype is useful in determining if various genetic defects are present.

Let's pretend that you have been given a chromosome sample obtained from an amniocentesis (the puncturing of the amniotic sac to remove fluid during pregnancy). Your job is to:

1. Sort the chromosomes by # according to the chart below.
2. Determine how many of each # are present. How many of each # should be present?
3. Determine if any of your chromosomes contain a mutation.
4. If a mutation is present, use the attached page to determine the type and extent of the genetic defect. Be ready to share your findings with the rest of the class.
5. Determine the sex: XX = female   XY = male

Color	Chromosome #	Number present in sample?	Mutation present?
Black (long)	2		
Black (medium)	9		
Blue	Y		
Bright Green (long)	8		
Bright Green (medium)	12		
Bright Green (short)	22		
Brown (long)	3		
Brown (medium)	16		
Brown (short)	17		
Dark Green (long)	6		
Dark Green (medium)	15		
Orange (long)	1		
Orange (medium)	11		
Orange (short)	21		
Pink	X		
Red (long)	7		
Red (medium)	10		
Red (short)	19		
White (long)	5		
White (medium)	13		
White (short)	18		
Yellow (long)	4		
Yellow (medium)	14		
Yellow (short)	20		

KARYOTYPE ACTIVITY

Sample # _____

Answer the following questions regarding your sample. Use an electronic resource to help you analyze your karyotype.

1. What is the sex of your sample? _____

2. Do any of your chromosomes contain a *mutation*? _____ If so, which one(s)? _____

3. Do you have any chromosomes that are incorrect in #? _____ If so, which one(s)? _____

4. Does your sample contain a genetic disorder? _____

   If so, which one? _____

DNA EXTRACTION LAB

© Valentina Razumova/
Shutterstock.com

INTRODUCTION

In this lab, we will do a simple DNA extraction experiment using a strawberry and common household items. Many plants are called *polyploidy*, meaning they have more than 2 sets of chromosomes. Commercially grown strawberries have 8 sets of 7 chromosomes, which means they have 56 chromosomes per cell.

LAB MATERIALS:

1 strawberry in a plastic cup
Snack-sized Ziploc bag
Measuring spoons or graduated cylinder
Dish soap (this will break down the phospholipid bilayer and proteins that compose the membranes of the cell)
Salt (this is used to keep the DNA from sticking together)
Distilled water (this is used for mixing)
Alcohol (this is used to clump the DNA and separate it from the mixture; DNA is not alcohol soluble)
1 coffee filter
1 test tube
1 paper clip

PROCEDURE:

1. Put the strawberry in the Ziploc bag.
2. Add ¼ tsp (0.25 mL) dish soap.
3. Add ¼ tsp (0.25 mL) salt.
4. Add ¾ tsp (4.5 mL) distilled water.
5. Remove all of the air from the Ziploc bag and close it.
6. Mix/mash the contents of the bag leaving no chunks.
7. Place the coffee filter on top of the paper cup.
8. Move the contents of the Ziploc bag to one corner of the bag. Cut the corner of the bag and empty the contents into the coffee filter.
9. Gently gather the ends of the coffee filter together and gently squeeze the strawberry juices through the filter and into the plastic cup.
10. Pour the filtrate from the cup into the test tube.
11. Add the alcohol to the test tube by pouring it GENTLY down the SIDE of the test tube.
12. Wait 5 minutes and you will begin to see white stringy material in the test tube. THIS IS DNA.
13. Straighten the paper clip you have been given and wind the DNA around the paper clip by inserting it into the test tube.

POSTLAB QUESTION

1. As far as procedure goes, is there anything you would have done differently to make this lab more accessible?

Label the structures in the following pictures.

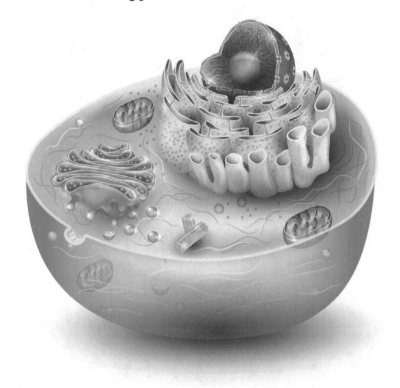

© Tefi/Shutterstock.com

nucleus   nucleolus   plasma membrane   golgi apparatus   endoplasmic reticulum
centrioles   mitochondria   cytoplasm   ribosomes

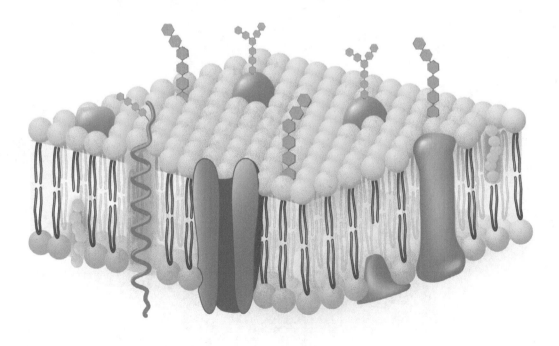

© marina_ua/Shutterstock.com

protein channel   hydrophilic heads   hydrophobic tails   glycolipid   carbohydrate

LAB: OSMOSIS EXPERIMENT

Your team will be assigned one of the following setups. A small piece of dialysis tubing will function as our model of a "cell." As you can see from this table, the ICF of the cells can vary as well as the ECF that we will be testing.

Table Number	Solution in the beaker (ECF)	Solution in the "cell" (ICF)	Prediction (gain or lose water from cell?)	Why?
A	water	100% sugar syrup		
B	water	50% sugar syrup/50% water		
C	10% salt water solution	water		
D	Seawater	water		
E	Phosphosoda solution	water		

DIRECTIONS:

1. Make your cell by wetting a small piece of dialysis tubing so that you can make it into a tube. Tie one end of the tube with the string. Fill your cell with your assigned ICF and tie the other end. Make sure to cut off any excess tubing and string.
2. Collect a 400-mL beaker and the appropriate ECF that you have been assigned.
3. Add approximately 150 mL of the appropriate ECF solution to the 400-mL beaker.
4. Use the balance to determine the weight of your "cell" and record the weight in the data table.
5. Place your cell into the beaker with the ECF.
6. After 10 minutes, gently remove your cell from the beaker and blot it dry on paper towels.
7. Weight your cell on the balance and record the weight in the data table below.
8. Put the cell back in the beaker for 10 more minutes (20 minutes total) and then repeat the blotting and weighing.
9. Put the cell back in the beaker for 10 more minutes (30 minutes total) and then repeat the blotting and weighing.

Time in minutes	Weight in grams	Change in weight in grams
0		
10		
20		
30		

10. Calculate the change in weight by finding the difference in weight between the original weight (weight at 0 minutes) and the final weight (weight at 30 minutes).

11. Now, calculate the percent change in weight for your cell.
    - <u>To calculate the percentage change:</u> Subtract the old from the new, then divide by the old value. If you have a negative value, this indicates a percentage decrease. If you have a positive number, this indicates a percentage increase. You can also go to www.percent-change.com to have it calculated for you.

12. Record the data from your team, and collect the data from the rest of the teams. Record all in the data table below.

    a. If a cell **lost weight**, the value for the change in weight and the % change in weight will be a **negative number** and should be preceded by a negative sign.
    b. If a cell **gained weight**, the value for the change in weight and the % change in weight will be a **positive number** and should be preceded by a positive sign.

Table #	Solution in Beaker (ECF)	Solution in Cell (ICF)	Change in weight	% change in weight
A	water	100% sugar syrup		
B	water	50% sugar syrup/ 50% water		
C	10% salt solution	water		
D	Seawater	water		
E	Phosphosoda solution	water		

Chapters 4 and 5 Lab

Tissues, and The Integumentary System

CHAPTER (4) LAB

TISSUES

Answer the following questions.

1. The study of tissues is called _____.

2. Give the definition of tissue:_____

3. What is a membrane? _____

_____

Match each term in column A with its description in column B.

Column A

A. simple squamous
B. nervous
C. transitional
D. stratified squamous
E. skeletal muscle
F. smooth muscle
G. cardiac muscle
H. matrix
I. fibroblast
J. areolar
K. adipose
L. dense fibrous
M. cartilage
N. bone
O. blood
P. squamous
Q. cuboidal
R. columnar
S. simple
T. stratified
U. cilia
V. pseudostratified

Column B

_____ 1. voluntary muscle
_____ 2. can be compact or cancellous (the hardest connective tissue)
_____ 3. describes multiple layers of cells
_____ 4. muscle of the heart
_____ 5. describes a cell that is long/tall
_____ 6. connective tissue of tendons and ligaments
_____ 7. describes a single layer of flat cells
_____ 8. tissue that sends electrical impulses
_____ 9. describes a cell that is flat
_____ 10. looks like multiple layers, but is one layer
_____ 11. loose connective tissue
_____ 12. found in the inner lining of the urinary bladder
_____ 13. cell that makes collagen
_____ 14. describes a single layer of cells
_____ 15. "hairy" extensions on cells membranes to sweep and trap
_____ 16. liquid connective tissue; cells suspended in liquid
_____ 17. nonliving, noncellular material between cells of connective tissue
_____ 18. multiple layers of flat cells
_____ 19. muscle that is involuntary and found in hollow organs
_____ 20. connective tissue that is strong and bendable; like in the ear
_____ 21. describes a cell that is square
_____ 22. also known as fat

CHEEK CELL LAB

PROCEDURE:

1. Use the toothpick provided to scrape some cells from the inside of your cheek.

2. Smear the cells from the toothpick onto the class slide provided.

3. Place a *very small* drop of methylene blue on the sample and place a cover slip on top.

4. Carefully blot the slide to remove any excess dye.

5. Look under the microscope at your cheek cells.

6. Draw what you see in the area provided.

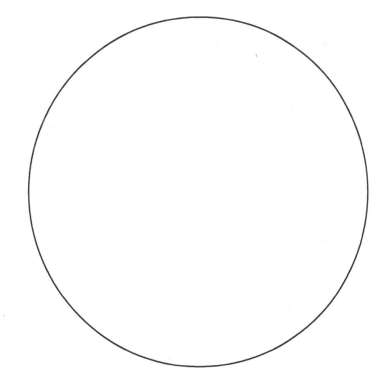

POST LAB QUESTIONS

1. Label the cell membrane on your illustration.

2. Label the nucleus on your illustration.

Complete the following questions.

1. What is connective tissue?

2. List the four major types of cells found in connective tissue, and then explain their function.

3. For each of the connective tissue types, give an example of where you would find each:

    a. loose (areolar):

    b. adipose:

    c. dense fibrous:

    d. cartilage:

    e. bone:

    f. blood:

4. List the three types of cartilage. Give an example of where you would find each in the body.

5. What is epithelial tissue?

6. For each of the epithelial tissue types, give an example of where you would find each:

    a. simple squamous:

    b. simple cuboidal:

    c. simple columnar:

    d. pseudostratified:

    e. stratified squamous:

    f. glandular epithelium:

    g. transitional:

7. What is the difference between endocrine glands and exocrine glands?

8. You have just landed a job in a laboratory that specializes in reading biopsies. Unfortunately, the lab is a mess (from the incompetent worker who was fired), and there are slides from seven patients scattered about. You have no way to identify the patients except for the reason of the biopsy. The slides are numbered, and your job is to fix the mess that was left for you—and make sure the correct report goes with the correct slide. Use the information provided, along with the slide depicting the epithelium, to match the correct slide number with the correct patient name.

Types of Epithelial Tissues	Where Found
Pseudostratified columnar	Respiratory tract and tubes of the male reproductive system
Stratified squamous	Ureter, urinary bladder, skin
Stratified cuboidal	Large ducts of glands of the endocrine system (hormone-producing glands)
Stratified columnar	Large ducts of salivary glands, uterus, pharynx (throat), urethra and vas deferens (both male)
Transitional	Bladder, renal pelvis of the kidney (where freshly made urine collects)
Simple columnar	Stomach, small intestine, uterus, fallopian tubes
Simple squamous	Lung (alveoli—small air sacs within the lung) and kidney
Simple cuboidal	Small ducts of exocrine glands (salivary, pancreatic, etc.)

Patient	Reason for Biopsy
Eugene Krabs	Patient complains of shortness of breath
Sylvia Jenkins	Ultrasound revealed abnormalities in the female reproductive tract
Patrick Starr	Blood in the urine
Jamaar Prince	Manual exam reveals abnormalities in the testes
Jose Padilla	Patient presents with an abnormality of the external surface of his upper back
Bruce Banner	Patient complains of upper, deep abdominal pain
Martha White	Suspected mass in the thyroid gland (an endocrine gland)

Record your answers here:

Slide #	Patient	Type of Epithelial Tissue
A		
B		
C		
D		
E		
F		
G		

Complete the following table by filling in the correct tissue type.

Description	Tissue Type
• contraction • three types • voluntary and involuntary	
• conducts electrical impulses • transmits information	
• glands are composed of this • lines hollow organs and passageways • covers exposed surfaces	
• most abundant tissue type • fills spaces • provides support • stores energy	

1. Describe a gap junction.

2. Describe a tight junction.

3. Give an example of where you would find each one.

Observe each of the following tissue types using the slides provided and a microscope. Sketch what you see for each tissue type. *Be sure to identify the source of the tissue.*

Skeletal muscle   Simple squamous tissue

Smooth muscle   Stratified squamous tissue

Cardiac muscle   Simple cuboidal tissue

Compact bone   Blood

Nervous tissue   Simple columnar tissue

                                                   Transitional epithelium

THE INTEGUMENTARY SYSTEM

Place the following in the correct order from most superficial to most deep.

_____ subcutaneous   _____ stratum spinosum   _____ dermis

_____ stratum basale   _____ stratum corneum   _____ stratum granulosum

Match each term in column A with its description in column B.

Column A

A. keratin
B. dermis
C. melanocytes
D. eccrine sweat gland
E. stratum corneum
F. collagen
G. sebaceous gland
H. follicle
I. fingerprints
J. stratum basale
K. apocrine sweat gland
L. melanin
M. subcutaneous
N. arrector pili muscle
O. sweat
P. nail
Q. sensory receptor
R. vitamin D
S. sebum
T. pore

Column B

_____ 1. outermost layer of epidermis
_____ 2. the medical term for an oil gland
_____ 3. a nutrient made in the skin from sunlight
_____ 4. protein that waterproofs the skin
_____ 5. pulls on hair to make it stand up; causes "goose bumps"
_____ 6. middle layer of the integument – where glands, etc. are found
_____ 7. deepest layer of epidermis
_____ 8. protein used to block UV radiation; gives skin its color
_____ 9. this gland secretes a thick, smelly fluid into the hair follicles
_____ 10. receives a stimulus of the skin
_____ 11. ridges in skin—everyone's are unique
_____ 12. a minute opening on the skin that delivers a substance to the surface
_____ 13. glands that secrete a watery substance directly to the skin for cooling
_____ 14. the type of oil secreted in the hair follicle
_____ 15. the layer with adipose tissue, nerve endings, and blood vessels
_____ 16. the main structural protein found in the skin
_____ 17. a substance to cool down the body
_____ 18. houses and supports the growing hair
_____ 19. modified epidermis that hardens at the ends of the fingers and toes
_____ 20. cell that makes melanin

Complete the following questions.

1. List the functions of the skin.

2. What is a melanocyte? What is melanin?

3. What is the purpose of collagen?

4. What are the two major layers of the dermis?

5. State the degrees of burn.

6. Describe the *function* of the following accessory structures found in skin:

    a. hair _____

    b. arrector pili muscle _____

    c. sebaceous gland _____

    d. sebum _____

    e. apocrine sweat gland _____

    f. merocrine/eccrine sweat gland _____

    g. nails _____

    h. sensory receptors _____

7. Identify the major characteristics of the following skin cancers. Which is most deadly?

    a. basal cell carcinoma _____

    b. squamous cell carcinoma _____

    c. malignant melanoma _____

8. Explain why fat-soluble drugs are preferred over water-soluble drugs for transdermal (through the skin) administration (e.g., nicotine patch).

Identify the parts of the skin here:

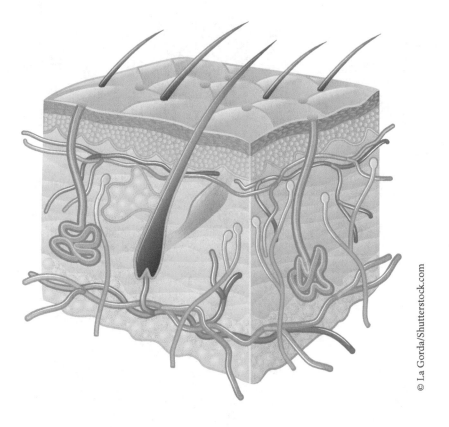

sebaceous gland   sudoriferous gland   hair follicle   hair shaft   melanocytes
epidermis   dermis   arector pili muscle   subcutaneous layer   pores
adipose tissue   blood vessels   nerve endings

UNDERSTANDING SKIN CANCER

Skin cancer symptoms vary from person to person. They may include:
- Change on the skin, such as a new spot or one that changes in size, shape, or color
- A sore that doesn't heal
- Spot or sore that changes in sensation, itchiness, tenderness, or pain
- Small, smooth, shiny, pale, or waxy lump
- Firm red lump that may bleed or develops a crust
- Flat, red spot that is rough, dry, or scaly

The three most common malignant skin cancers are *basal cell cancer*, *squamous cell cancer*, and *melanoma*, each of which is named after the type of skin cell from which it arises.

SKIN CANCER FACTS:

- Melanoma is less common than both basal cell carcinoma and squamous cell carcinoma, but it is the most serious.
- It is the second most common cancer in young adults aged 15 to 34.
- Most cases are caused by overexposure to ultraviolet (UV) rays from the sun or tanning beds.
- Non-melanoma skin cancers are the most common skin cancers.
- The majority of skin cancers are basal cell carcinomas, which are usually localized and caused by much exposure to UV light.

Basal cell carcinoma:
- Presents as a raised, smooth, pearly bump on the sun-exposed skin of the head, neck, or shoulders.
- Sometimes small blood vessels can be seen within the tumor.
- Crusting and bleeding in the center of the tumor frequently develops.
- It is often mistaken for a sore that does not heal.
- This form of skin cancer is the **least deadly**.
- With proper treatment, can be completely eliminated, often without scarring.

Squamous cell carcinoma:
- Commonly a red, scaling, thickened patch on sun-exposed skin.
- Some are firm hard nodules and dome shaped, appearing as a small tumor.
- Ulceration and bleeding may occur around the entire tumor.
- If not treated, it may develop into a large mass.
- The second most common skin cancer.
- **It is dangerous, but not nearly as dangerous as a melanoma.**

Melanoma:
- Brown to black looking lesions.
- A few melanomas are pink, red, or fleshy in color, which tend to be more aggressive.
- Warning signs of malignant melanoma include:
  1. Change in the size, shape, color, or elevation of a mole.
  2. New pain, itching, ulceration, or bleeding of an existing mole.
  3. The appearance of a new mole during adulthood.

An often-used mnemonic is "ABCDE"
A= "asymmetrical"
B= "borders" (irregular)
C= "color" (variegated)
D= "diameter" (larger than a pencil eraser)
E= "evolving" (changing) or "elevated"

Using what you have learned from the Understanding Skin Cancer page, diagnose the type of skin condition from the presented slides. The conditions can be:

- basal cell carcinoma (BCC)
- squamous cell carcinoma (SCC)
- malignant melanoma (MM)
- normal mole(N)

1. _____

2. _____

3. _____

4. _____

5. _____

6. _____

7. _____

8. _____

9. _____

10. _____

Identify the five layers of the epidermis from the most superficial to the deepest. Remember this saying: Come Let's Get Some Beer.

1.

2.

3.

4.

5.

UNIT 3

Chapters 6-8 Lab

The Skeletal System, and The Articular System

THE SKELETAL SYSTEM

INTRODUCTION TO THE SKELETAL SYSTEM

1. List the functions of the skeletal system.

2. List the bones of the axial skeleton.

3. List the bones of the appendicular skeleton.

Match each term in column A with its description in column B.

Column A

A. epiphysis
B. diaphysis
C. compact bone
D. spongy bone
E. epiphyseal plate
F. lacunae
G. lamellae
H. canaliculi
I. osteon
J. trabeculae
K. osteoblast
L. central canal
M. perforating canal
N. osteoclast
O. calcium phosphate
P. collagen
Q. intramembranous ossification
R. endochondral ossification

Column B

_____ 1. cartilage between epiphysis and diaphysis
_____ 2. cylindrical, concentric layers around central canal
_____ 3. ossification of long bones
_____ 4. end of long bone
_____ 5. bone cell that breaks up bone
_____ 6. type of bone that is rigid, solid, and hard
_____ 7. found in the medullary cavity and ends of bone; looks like sponge
_____ 8. mineral matrix of the bone
_____ 9. protein found in bone matrix
_____ 10. middle of long bone; the shaft
_____ 11. term that describes the ossification of flat bones
_____ 12. connects periosteum blood vessels to Haversian canal (a pathway)
_____ 13. provides strength to cancellous bone; looks like a web
_____ 14. encompasses an osteocyte
_____ 15. bone-forming cell
_____ 16. center of osteon; contains blood vessels
_____ 17. microscopic canals of the lamellae that interconnect lacunae
_____ 18. basic, functional unit of compact bone

Complete the following questions.

1. Describe the following parts:

   a. periosteum _____

   b. compact bone _____

   c. spongy bone _____

2. What is the difference between a tendon and a ligament?

3. What would happen to bone if the following were *lacking* in the diet?

   a. protein _____

   b. calcium _____

   c. vitamin D _____

4. Describe the functions of the osteoblast and the osteoclast.

5. What is ossification?

On the bone shown, label the following structures:

spongy bone   compact bone   medullary cavity
epiphysis (you will need to draw this in)   metaphysis   diaphysis

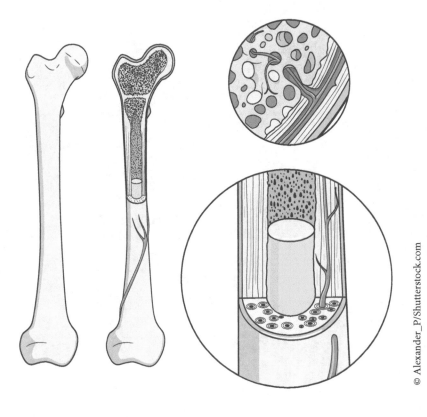

© Alexander_P/Shutterstock.com

Number the following in the correct order of the process of ossification.

_____ secondary ossification   _____ birth: epiphyses are cartilage
_____ cartilage ossified as we age   _____ childhood: epiphyseal plate grows
_____ fetal cartilage   _____ ends after adolescence
_____ periosteum starts making compact bone

Label the skeleton using the list on the following page:

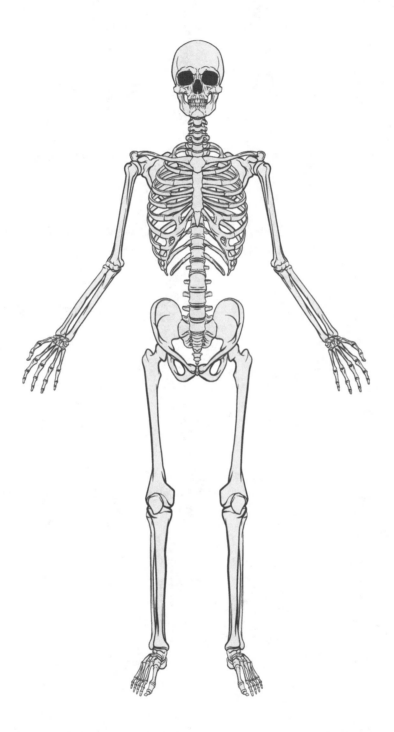

INTRODUCTION TO THE APPENDICULAR AND AXIAL SKELETON

Using the skeleton, identify the following bones of the <u>appendicular</u> skeleton:

1. clavicle
2. scapula
3. humerus
4. ulna
5. radius
6. carpals (do not worry about naming each of those individual bones right now)
7. metacarpals
8. phalanges of the hand
9. ilium
10. ischium
11. femur
12. patella
13. tibia
14. fibula
15. tarsals (do not worry about naming each of those individual bones right now)
16. metatarsals
17. phalanges of the foot

Using the skeleton, identify the following bones of the <u>axial</u> skeleton:

1. sternum
2. ribs
3. cervical vertebrae
4. thoracic vertebrae
5. lumbar vertebrae
6. sacrum
7. coccyx
8. mandible
9. maxilla

Label the skull bones. Use the structures guide on page 51 as your guide.

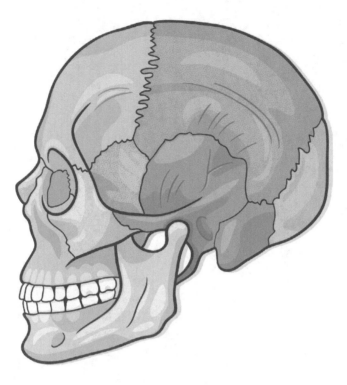

© Igor Zakowski/Shutterstock.com

Label the parts of the vertebra. Use the structures guide on page 52 as your guide.

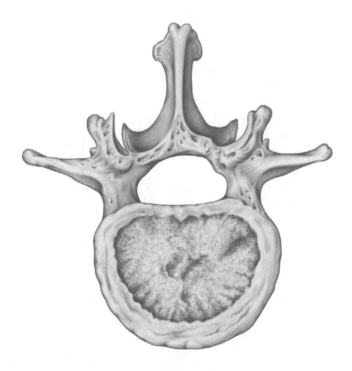

© stihii/Shutterstock.com

Label the parts of the inferior skull (also label the foramen magnum). Use the structures list on page 52 as your guide.

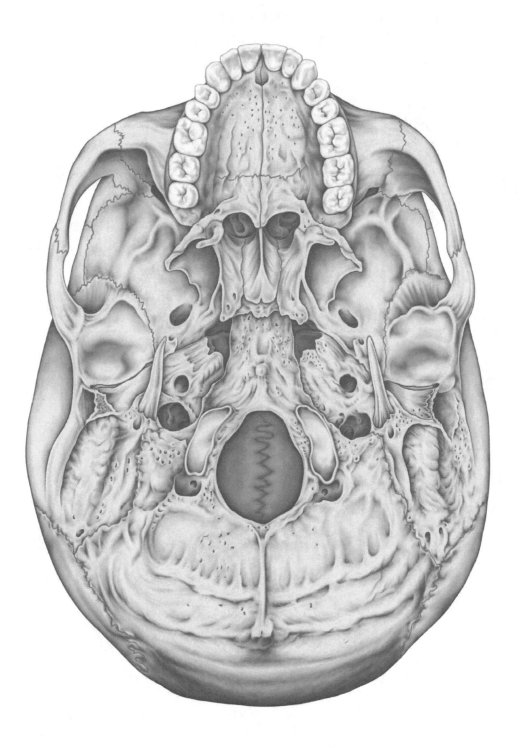

© stihii/Shutterstock.com

SLIPPERY SURFACE: FRACTURE AND BONE REPAIR CASE STUDY

Megan, age 10, is in the fifth grade. During recess one day, she was climbing on a wooden play structure. It had just rained, so the wood was slippery. When she got to the top step, she slipped and fell on her right arm and then bumped her head on the ground.

The paramedics arrive and notice that Megan's forearm is deformed and appears as though pieces of bone are protruding from the skin. Associated with this is a fairly large wound. Additionally, her teacher states that she was "knocked out" for a minute or two after the fall. Megan is alert but appears to be somewhat dazed. She does not complain about pain in her arm, but reports that her head hurts.

When Megan arrives at the hospital, doctors determine that she has the following:

1. a compound fracture of the diaphysis of the right radius and ulna
2. a concussion
3. several contusions on her back and neck

SHORT ANSWER QUESTIONS

1. Define the following terms used in the case and also in associated questions:

    a. concussion

    b. fracture

    c. contusion

    d. diaphysis

2. How would you classify the shape of the bones that Megan fractured?

3. Which anatomical structures in Megan's compact bone contain blood vessels?

4. It was decided that Megan's arm would not be casted right away. Instead, it will be splinted and placed in a sling for a week or two. Why is it not a good idea to place a cast on Megan's arm right away?

5. What is osteoclasis and how is it involved in bone repair?

WRITE YOUR OWN GROUP CASE STUDY

Using the previous case about 10-year-old Megan as an example, write your own case study relating to the skeletal system. Your group will be assigned a situation and terms that you will use as your guide. Be sure to include the following:

Patient age
Cause of the injury
Details of the injury
Diagnosis
Any other interesting details you deem necessary

You do not need to write questions at the end.

IN-CLASS FRACTURE EXERCISE

Type of Fracture	Description
Transverse fracture	
Displaced fracture	
Compression fracture	
Spiral fracture	
Epiphyseal fracture	
Comminuted fracture	
Greenstick fracture	
Colles fracture	
Pott's fracture	

IDENTIFICATION OF FRACTURES:

1. _____

2. _____

3. _____

4. _____

5. _____

6. _____

7. _____

8. _____

9. _____

LAB: Identify the following bones, bone markings, and joints on models. Place a ✔ in the box as you find each one.

Bone Markings

Marking	Bone	✔	Marking	✔	Bone
process			sinus		
line			tubercle		
head			spine		
ramus			facet		
tuberosity			fossa		
trochanter			crest		
neck			epicondyle		
condyle			foramen		

Bones of the Skull

Bone	✔	Bone	✔
frontal		temporal	
sphenoid		nasal	
maxillary		vomer	
palatine		occipital	
parietal		mandible	
ethmoid		zygomatic	
lacrimal			

Processes, Sutures, and Foramen of the Skull

Marking	✔	Marking	✔
foramen magnum		styloid process	
sella turcica		jugular foramen	
external auditory meatus		mastoid process	
occipital condyles		zygomatic arch	
perpendicular plate		cribriform plate	
squamous suture		coronal suture	
lambdoid suture		sagittal suture	

Vertebrae

Vertebra	✔	Marking	✔
C1 (atlas) and C2 (axis)		body	
cervical		spinous process	
thoracic		transverse process	
lumbar		dens	
sacrum		vertebral foramen	
coccyx		pedicle	

Sternum   **Ribs**

Marking	✔	Bone	✔
body		true ribs	
manubrium		false ribs	
xiphoid process			

Scapula

Clavicle

Marking	✓	Marking	✓
acromion		acromial end	
coracoid process		sterna end	
spine of scapula			
glenoid cavity/fossa			

Humerus

Marking	✓	Marking	✓
head		deltoid tuberosity	
neck		coronoid fossa	
capitulum		olecranon fossa	
trochlea		radial fossa	

Ulna

Radius

Marking	✓	Marking	✓
head		head	
olecranon process		styloid process	
trochlear notch			

Carpals

Metacarpals and Phalanges

Bone	✓	Bone	✓	Bone	✓
scaphoid		trapezium		metacarpals 1-5	
lunate		trapezoid		phalanges 1-5	
triquetrum		capitate			
pisiform		hamate			

Pelvic Bones

Marking	✓	Marking	✓
ilium		acetabulum	
ischium		greater sciatic notch	
pubic symphysis		iliac fossa	
obturator foramen		iliac crest	

Femur

Marking	✓	Marking	✓
head		greater trochanter	
neck		lesser trochanter	
lateral condyle		patellar surface (and patella)	
medial condyle		intercondylar fossa	

Tibia   **Fibula**

Marking	✓	Marking	✓
medial malleolus		head	
tibial tuberosity		lateral malleolus	

Tarsals   **Metatarsals and Phalanges**

Bone	✓	Bone	✓	Bone	✓
talus		intermediate cuneiform		metatarsals 1-5	
calcaneus		lateral cuneiform		phalanges 1-5	
navicular		cuboid			
medial cuneiform					

THE ARTICULAR SYSTEM

Match the bone markings in column A with the correct bone in column B. Some will be used more than once.

Column A
1. femur
2. humerus
3. fibula
4. tibia
5. scapula
6. radius
7. ulna
8. ilium
9. sternum
10. clavicle
11. temporal bone
12. occipital bone

Column B
_____ capitulum
_____ trochlear notch
_____ external auditory meatus
_____ manubrium
_____ foramen magnum
_____ coracoid process
_____ greater trochanter
_____ deltoid tuberosity
_____ lesser trochanter
_____ greater sciatic notch
_____ acromion
_____ xiphoid process
_____ obturator foramen
_____ olecranon process
_____ ulnar notch
_____ neck
_____ lateral malleolus
_____ medial malleolus
_____ anterior margin
_____ sternal and acromial ends

Complete the following questions.

1. Describe the degree of movement associated with the following types of joints:

   a. synarthrosis _____

   b. amphiarthrosis _____

   c. diarthrosis _____

2. Describe the degree of movement associated with the following types of joints AND give an example:

   a. fibrous _____

   b. cartilaginous _____

   c. synovial _____

3. Give an example of where you would find each of the following synovial joints:

    a. hinge_____

    b. pivot_____

    c. ball and socket_____

4. Describe the following parts of the synovial joint:

    a. capsule_____

    b. membrane_____

    c. fluid _____

    d. articular cartilage_____

    e. meniscus_____

    f. locations in body where menisci found _____

    g. bursa _____

    h. ligament _____

Label the structures on the knee joint shown using the structures list from #4 above.

Anatomy of the Knee Joint

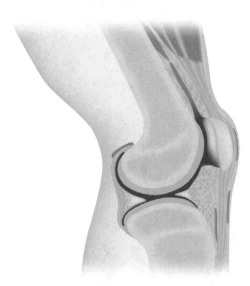

Match each type of movement in column A with its description in column B.

Column A

A. flexion
B. extension
C. hyperextension
D. abduction
E. adduction
F. medial rotation
G. lateral rotation
H. elevation
I. depression
J. protraction of mandible
K. retraction of mandible
L. dorsiflexion of foot
M. plantar flexion of foot
N. inversion of foot
O. eversion of foot
P. supination
Q. pronation
R. circumduction

Column B

_____ 1. twist foot, turns sole inward
_____ 2. move structure superiorly
_____ 3. move mandible anteriorly
_____ 4. internal, inward rotation
_____ 5. rotation of forearm makes palm face anteriorly
_____ 6. flex ankle, elevate sole
_____ 7. movement away from longitudinal axis of body
_____ 8. movement decreases angle between bones
_____ 9. rotation of forearm makes palm face posteriorly
_____ 10. external, outward rotation
_____ 11. movement increases angle between bones
_____ 12. to move mandible posteriorly
_____ 13. extension past anatomical position
_____ 14. movement toward longitudinal axis of body
_____ 15. move structure inferiorly
_____ 16. twist foot, turns sole outward
_____ 17. move arm in a loop
_____ 18. extend ankle, elevate heel

CLASSIFYING JOINTS: Fibrous joints: Use skull and teeth models. Check each one as you find it.

Joint Type	✔
cartilaginous	
ball and socket joint	
hinge joint	
pivot joint	
fibrous joint (sutures of the skull)	
gomphosis	
temporomandibular joint	

Name _____

MOCK LAB PRACTICAL ANSWER SHEET

TABLE A

1. _____
2. _____
3. _____
4. _____
5. _____
6. _____
7. _____
8. _____
9. _____

TABLE B

1. _____
2. _____
3. _____
4. _____
5. _____
6. _____
7. _____
8. _____
9. _____

TABLE C

1. _____
2. _____
3. _____
4. _____
5. _____
6. _____
7. _____
8. _____
9. _____

TABLE D

1. _____
2. _____
3. _____
4. _____
5. _____
6. _____
7. _____
8. _____
9. _____

TABLE E

1. _____
2. _____
3. _____
4. _____
5. _____
6. _____
7. _____
8. _____
9. _____

UNIT 4

Chapters 9 and 10 Lab

The Muscular System

INTRODUCTION TO THE MUSCULAR SYSTEM

Place the following in the correct order from a nerve impulse to a muscle contraction.

_____ calcium frees actin   _____ acetylcholine released   _____ neuron action potential
_____ acetylcholine receptor   _____ synapse   _____ myosin pulls actin
_____ calcium released   _____ impulse through T tubules   _____ Z lines closer together

Match each term in column A with its description in column B.

Column A   Column B

A. fascia   _____ 1. major muscle pulling bone
B. antagonist   _____ 2. constant, partial contraction; used in posture
C. acetylcholine   _____ 3. muscle pulls bone to increase angle of joint
D. origin   _____ 4. nerve cell sending impulses to muscle
E. muscle tone   _____ 5. one motor neuron and several muscle fibers
F. actin   _____ 6. block active sites on actin
G. tendon   _____ 7. organelle that stores calcium in muscle fiber
H. prime mover   _____ 8. transition point between neuron and muscle fiber
I. motor neuron   _____ 9. connective tissue binding muscle to surroundings
J. sarcomere   _____ 10. end of muscle that pulls the bone
K. tropomyosin   _____ 11. muscle pulls bone to decrease angle of joint
L. extensibility   _____ 12. muscle tension stays same, muscle length changes
M. insertion   _____ 13. thick protein filament in muscle fiber
N. contractility   _____ 14. opposite muscle during flexion
O. synapse   _____ 15. myosin heads pulling on actin to shorten sarcomere
P. extend   _____ 16. provides energy for contraction
Q. myosin   _____ 17. neurotransmitter used at synapse
R. excitability   _____ 18. used to pull bone from muscle
S. isotonic   _____ 19. minimum impulse to create a reaction
T. sarcoplasmic reticulum   _____ 20. end of muscle that is stationary
U. isometric   _____ 21. the ability to respond to electrical stimulus
V. ATP   _____ 22. the ability to be stretched
W. flex   _____ 23. the functional unit of muscle fiber; Z line to Z line
X. motor unit   _____ 24. muscle length stays same, muscle tension changes
Y. threshold   _____ 25. ability to shorten and have force when stimulated
Z. power stroke   _____ 26. thin protein filament in muscle fiber

Complete the following questions.

1. List the functions of the muscular system.

2. Describe the following:

   epimysium =

   perimysium =

   endomysium =

3. What is the difference between tendon and aponeurosis?

4. What is the "all or none response"?

5. Explain the following energy supply periods:

   a. immediate energy

   b. short-term energy

   c. long-term energy

6. List some possible causes of muscle fatigue.

7. What is oxygen debt?

8. How does the muscle respond to increasing stimulus strength?

IDENTIFICATION OF STRUCTURES FROM A MICROSCOPIC VIEW

Shown is a low-powered micrograph of a neuromuscular junction.

Identify and label each of the following:

1. motor end plate
2. axon of motor neuron
3. skeletal muscle
4. striations present in skeletal muscle

© Christopher Meade/Shutterstock.com

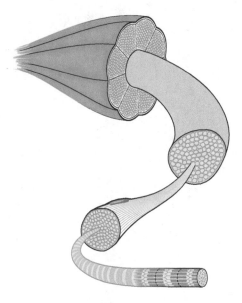

© Blamb/Shutterstock.com

<u>**Identify these regions:**</u> **Z line   H zone   I band   A band**   **Show where each sarcomere is located.**

Label the individual structures of the muscle:

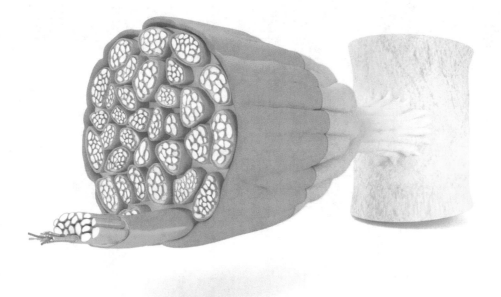

© Anton Nalivayko/Shutterstock.com

epimysium   perimysium   endomysium   fascicle   tendon   myofibrils

Draw the graphic depiction of repeated stimulation for each of the contraction types. Use the diagram in your textbook as your guide.

TENSION	Treppe	Wave summation
	Incomplete tetanus	Complete tetanus
	TIME	

IDENTIFICATION OF THE MUSCLES

Label the anterior muscles. Use the list on page 68 as your guide.

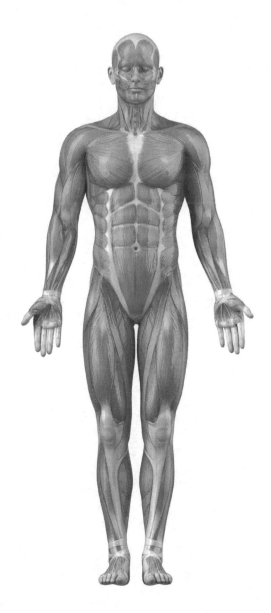

Label the posterior muscles. Use the list on page 68 as your guide.

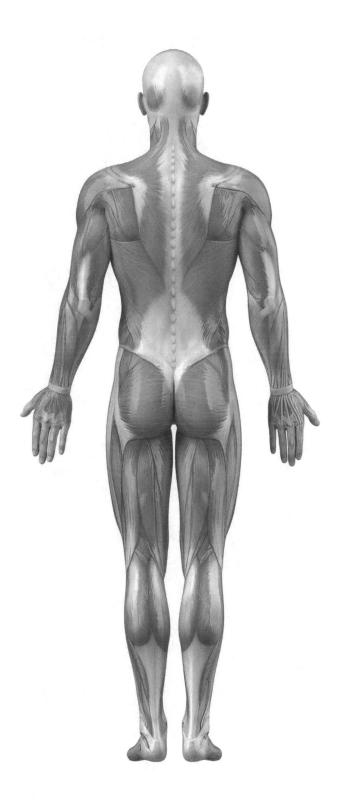

Match each muscle name in column A to its function in column B.

<u>Column A</u>   <u>Column B</u>

A. orbicularis oculi   _____ 1. elevates mandible
B. masseter   _____ 2. laterally rotate and flex head
C. buccinator   _____ 3. extend head and vertebral column
D. orbicularis oris   _____ 4. closes eye
E. sternocleidomastoid   _____ 5. draws angle of mouth for smiling
F. splenius capitis   _____ 6. closes & protrudes lips
G. temporalis   _____ 7. elevates and retracts mandible
H. zygomaticus major   _____ 8. raises eyebrows
I. frontalis   _____ 9. whistling, blowing & sucking actions

<u>Column A</u>   <u>Column B</u>

A. pectoralis major   _____ 1. compress abdomen and flexes vertebral column
B. serratus anterior   _____ 2. elevates and depresses ribs
C. abdominal muscles   _____ 3. extends, adducts and medially rotates arm
D. spinalis muscles   _____ 4. abducts scapula and rotates it upward
E. external intercostals   _____ 5. extends arm at shoulder joint
F. internal intercostals   _____ 6. rotate, adduct and depress scapula
G. teres major   _____ 7. extends the spine and maintain posture
H. trapezius   _____ 8. draws ribs together during forced exhalation
I. latissimus dorsi   _____ 9. adducts and medially rotates arm
J. pectoralis minor   _____ 10. abducts scapula and rotates it downward

Match each muscle name in column A to its function in column B.

Column A   Column B

A. deltoid   _____ 1. extends forearm
B. biceps brachii   _____ 2. extends and laterally rotates thigh
C. triceps brachii   _____ 3. adducts, flexes and rotates thigh
D. brachioradialis   _____ 4. dorsiflexion and inversion of the foot
E. psoas major   _____ 5. supinates and pronates forearm
F. adductor longus and magnus   _____ 6. weakly flexes leg at knee joint
G. gracilis   _____ 7. abducts and medially rotates arm
H. sartorius   _____ 8. flexes and abducts thigh
I. quadriceps   _____ 9. abducts and medially rotates thigh
J. tibialis anterior   _____ 10. flexes forearm
K. hamstrings   _____ 11. flexes leg and knee joint
L. gastrocnemius and soleus   _____ 12. plantar flexion of the foot
M. tensor fasciae latae   _____ 13. flexes and laterally rotates thigh
N. gluteus maximus   _____ 14. flexes leg and extends the thigh
O. gluteus medius   _____ 15. extends leg at knee joint

LAB: Identify the following muscles on the models. Place a ✔ in the box as you find each one.

Muscles of the head, neck, face	✔	Muscles of the head, neck, face	✔
orbicularis oculi		frontalis	
orbicularis oris		temporalis	
masseter		buccinator	
splenius capitis		platysma	
zygomaticus major		sternocleidomastoid	

Muscles of the chest, abdomen, back	✔	Muscles of the chest, abdomen, back	✔
pectoralis major		spinalis muscles	
trapezius		internal oblique	
serratus anterior		external oblique	
rectus abdominis		transverse abdominis	
latissimus dorsi		intercostals	
rhomboids		psoas major	

Muscles of the arm and shoulder	✔	Muscles of the arm and shoulder	✔
deltoid		teres major	
supraspinatus		infraspinatus	
triceps brachii		subscapularis	
teres minor		brachioradialis	

Muscles of the thigh, leg, hip	✔	Muscles of the thigh, leg, hip	✔
gracilis		adductor longus	
sartorius		rectus femoris	
biceps femoris		tibialis anterior	
gastrocnemius		soleus	
gluteus maximus		gluteus medius	

Name _____

Obtain a microscope slide of each of the 3 types of muscle. Sketch what you see in the areas below. Be sure to label the intercalated disks and the striations on the cardiac muscle sketch and the striations on the skeletal muscle sketch.

Skeletal muscle	Cardiac muscle	Smooth muscle

CHICKEN WING DISSECTION

MATERIALS:

Dissecting pan
Scissors
Scalpel
Chicken wing
Paper towels
Cleaner
Pins

PROCEDURE:

1. Identify the dorsal and ventral sides of the wing. The dorsal side will have the thicker skin. Draw and label what you see.

2. Pin your wing with the dorsal side down. Slit the skin at the wing edges with the scalpel and remove the skin from the ventral side. Do not cut the underlying white connective tissue at the wing tip.

3. Pin your wing with the ventral side down. Remove the skin from the dorsal side of the arm.

4. Remove the pins.

5. Identify the biceps muscle in the arm. Hold the humerus and pull on the proximal end of the biceps. Describe what happened.

6. Look at the attachment of the biceps muscle to the bones. What bones does the biceps attach?

7. Identify the triceps muscle in the arm. Hold the humerus and pull on the proximal end of the triceps. Describe what happened.

8. Look for the attachment of the triceps to the bone. What bones does the triceps muscle attach?

9. Squeeze the triceps and hold it still. With your other hand, pull on the biceps at the proximal end. Describe what happens to the elbow joint when <u>both</u> of these muscles are contracted.

10. Move the elbow back and forth. What type of joint is this?

11. Stretch the chicken wing out so that the elbow joint is stressed.

12. Carefully cut across the joint capsule at the stressed tissue. Note the interior space as the joint opens. Extend the cut until you can find the three shiny, strong surfaces. One surface will be on the humerus, one on the ulna, and one on the radius.

13. What are the shiny, strong surfaces that withstand pressure?

14. What relationship did you see between the point of a muscle's attachment and the joint that it moves?

UNIT 5

Chapters 11-15 Lab

The Nervous System

INTRODUCTION TO THE NERVOUS SYSTEM

Place the following events in the correct order.

_____ brain   _____ motor neuron   _____ ascending spinal cord
_____ receptor   _____ effector organ
_____ descending spinal cord   _____ sensory neuron

Match each term in column A with its description in column B.

Column A   Column B

A. myelin sheath   _____ 1. relay neuron in the spinal cord and brain
B. dendrites   _____ 2. potassium ions exit; voltage changes back
C. neurotransmitter   _____ 3. part of neuron that contains the nucleus
D. interneuron   _____ 4. processes from the cell body; communication point with axon
E. receptor   _____ 5. special cells used for smell
F. axon   _____ 6. classification of a neuron with multiple pathways
G. action potential   _____ 7. support cell for neurons
H. multipolar neuron   _____ 8. there are 31 pairs of these
I. depolarization   _____ 9. a small gap between neurons; neurotransmitter is released here
J. cell body   _____ 10. fatlike covering of an axon; speeds up transmission
K. unipolar neuron   _____ 11. the neuron that releases a neurotransmitter
L. glial cell   _____ 12. contains rods and cones for vision
M. reflex arc   _____ 13. classification of a neuron with a single pathway
N. olfactory   _____ 14. long, tail-like part of a neuron; transmits impulse
O. synapse   _____ 15. organ that converts sound energy to electrical energy
P. repolarization   _____ 16. voluntary part of the nervous system; skeletal muscle movement
Q. retina   _____ 17. when the resting potential changes to conduct electricity
R. postsynaptic neuron   _____ 18. collection of spinal nerves for a specific area
S. cochlea   _____ 19. sensory neuron to interneuron to motor neuron
T. spinal nerves   _____ 20. chemical messenger used at synapse
U. presynaptic neuron   _____ 21. the neuron that receives a neurotransmitter
V. somatic   _____ 22. sodium ions enter; voltage changes
W. plexus   _____ 23. a structure that receives the stimulus

Place the following in the correct order of neuron conduction.

_____ Depolarization   _____ Resting Potential   _____ Threshold exceeded   _____ Na-K Pump
_____ Repolarization   _____ Sodium moves in   _____ Potassium moves out   _____ Stimulus

Complete the following questions.

1. What are oligodendrocytes and Schwann cells?

2. What is the difference between gray matter and white matter?

3. State the location and layers of the meninges. What is the purpose of the meninges and cerebral spinal fluid?

4. Define peripheral nervous system and central nervous system.

5. Explain what it means for a neuron to be at "resting potential." Then, explain how a neuron generates and propagates an action potential.

6. Describe the general functions of neurotransmitters. Identify three important neurotransmitters.

7. Describe the role of the autonomic nervous system. Then, explain the role of the sympathetic and parasympathetic subsystems.

CHAPTERS 12-16 LAB

THE BRAIN, SPINAL CORD, CRANIAL NERVES, GENERAL SENSES, AND THE AUTONOMIC NERVOUS SYSTEM

Match each cranial nerve in column A with its description in column B.

Column A
A. olfactory
B. optic
C. oculomotor
D. trochlear
E. trigeminal
F. abducens
G. facial
H. vestibulocochlear
I. glossopharyngeal
J. vagus
K. accessory
L. hypoglossal

Column B
_____ 1. sensations of face, taste, chewing, movement of lower jaw
_____ 2. lateral and downward movement of the eye
_____ 3. swallowing; sternocleidomastoid and trapezius movement
_____ 4. hearing and equilibrium
_____ 5. swallowing, speech, pulmonary, cardiovascular, GI, etc.
_____ 6. swallowing, salivation, gag, tongue sensation
_____ 7. vision
_____ 8. most movements of the eye; eyelid control
_____ 9. tongue movement
_____ 10. sense of smell
_____ 11. facial expressions, tear and salivary gland secretion, taste
_____ 12. eye movement; fixation on an object

Identify each of the following cranial nerves as either sensory, motor, or both.

Nerve	S, M, or B?
Olfactory	
Optic	
Oculomotor	
Trochlear	
Trigeminal	
Abducens	
Facial	
Vestibulocochlear	
Glossopharyngeal	
Vagus	
Accessory	
Hypoglossal	

CRANIAL NERVE FUNCTION TESTS

Nerve	#	Features	Normal Response	Participant Findings
Olfactory	I	Ask the participant to close their eyes and smell a substance with each nostril separately. Use 2 substances.	Participant is able to identify each smell with each nostril with their eyes closed.	
Optic	II	Provide adequate lighting and ask participant to read something held at a 14 inch distance	Participant should be able to read with each eye.	
Oculomotor	III	Shine a penlight on the pupil to test for **light reaction**. Next, for **accommodation**, ask the participant to look at a near object and then at a far object. Alternate this 3 times and then move an object toward's the participants nose and have them follow it with their eyes.	Illuminated and non-illuminated pupils should constrict. Pupils should constrict when looking at a near object and dilate when looking at a far object.	
Trochlear	IV	Shine a penlight 1 inch from the participant's eyes. Ask the participant to follow the light as you move it up, down, sideways and diagonally.	Participant should be able to follow the light with their eyes.	
Trigeminal	V	Ask the participant to look upwards. At the same time, gently and lightly touch the lateral sclera to elicit the blink response. Next, to test for light touch sensation, gently swipe a Q-tip across their forehead. To test for deep pressure sensation, have client close their eyes and press the forehead with the blunt end of a probe. Finally, test the participant for the ability to identify warmth and coldness.	Participant should blink and be able to identify and respond to each of the touch sensations.	
Abducens	VI	Shine a penlight 1 inch from the participant's eyes. Ask the participant to follow the light as you move it up, down, sideways and diagonally.	Both eyes should move in unison.	

Nerve	#	Features	Normal Response	Participant Findings
Facial	VII	Ask participant to smile, raise their eyebrows, frown and puff out their cheeks. Next, ask participant to identify various tastes placed on the tip and sides of the tongue.	Participant should be able to perform all facial movements and correctly identify each of the tastes.	
Vestibuloco-chlear	VIII	Ask the participant to cover one ear. Place a ticking watch about 1 ½ inches from the covered ear. Ask if they can hear the watch. Repeat with the other ear. Next, to assess balance, ask the participant to walk across the room. Observe the gait.	The participant should be able to hear the watch from both ears. The participant should have upright posture, a steady gait and be able to maintain balance.	
Glossopha-ryngeal	IX	Ask the participant to yawn while you observe the upward movement of the soft palate. Next, ask the participant to swallow.	The participant should have upward movement of the soft palate while yawning. The participant should be able to swallow without difficulty.	
Vagus	X	Ask the participant to swallow a sip of water while you observe. Next, ask the participant to recite the alphabet.	The participant should be able to swallow without difficulty and audibly speak the alphabet.	
Accessory	XI	Ask the participant to shrug their shoulders while you apply resistance to them. Ask participant to turn their head to one side while you apply resistance. Repeat with the other side.	The participant should be able to symmetrically shrug their shoulders and turn their head from side to side against resistance.	
Hypoglossal	XII	Ask the participant to stick out their tongue. Next, have them move their tongue side to side.	The participant's tongue should be straight out and be able to easily move from side to side.	

Examiner: _____   Participant: _____

LAB: Identify the following parts of the brain on the models, then check each one.

Structure/Region	✔	Structure/Region	✔
gyri		sulci	
central sulcus		lateral sulcus	
longitudinal fissure		cerebral cortex and cerebrum	
cerebral hemispheres		corpus callosum	
midbrain		pons	
medulla oblongata		cerebellum	
thalamus		hypothalamus	
ventricles		occipital lobe	
temporal lobes		frontal lobe	
parietal lobes		pituitary gland	

LAB: Identify the following parts of the spinal cord on the model, then check each one.

Structure/Region	✔	Structure/Region	✔
central canal		ventral root	
dorsal root		dorsal root ganglion	
areas of white matter		areas of gray matter	
spinal nerve		anterior median fissure	
posterior median sulcus			

Label the features of the brain. Use the structures list on the previous page as your guide.

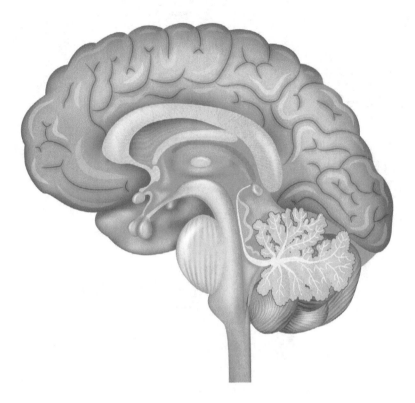

© Tefi/Shutterstock.com

Using arrows, draw the flow of the cerebral spinal fluid circulation. Label each ventricle and the cerebral aqueduct:

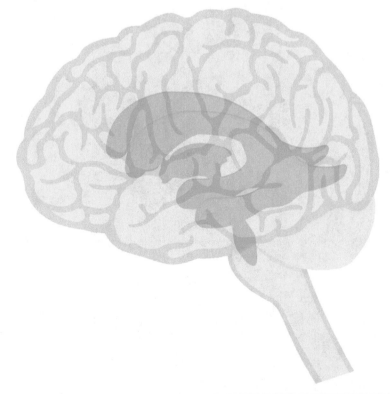

© joshya/Shutterstock.com

Label the features of the spinal cord cross section. Use the structures list on page 78 as your guide.

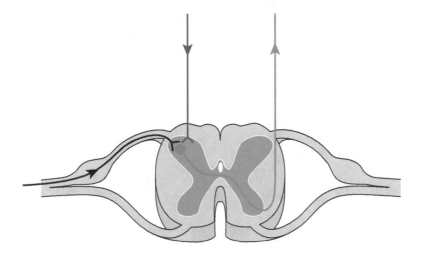

© Blamb/Shutterstock.com

Label the components of the pathway shown:

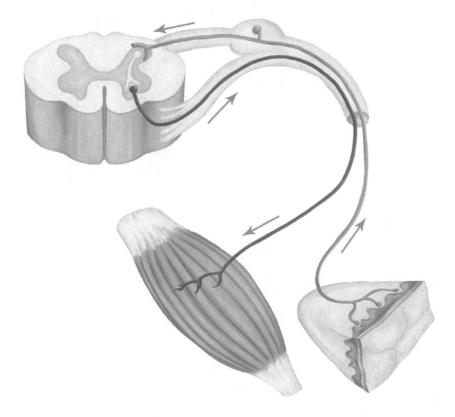

© stihii/Shutterstock.com

Identify the following on the brain diagram shown:

4 lobes of the brain   visual receiving area   auditory association area   written speech area
speech comprehension area   auditory receiving area   motor speech area   primary motor area
primary sensory area   central sulcus

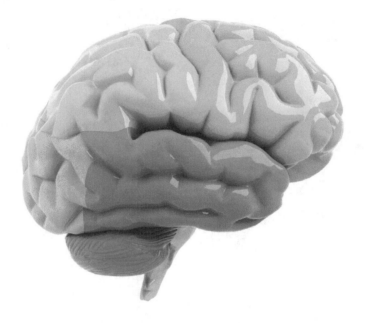

© anna–nt/Shutterstock.com

Identify the following on the brain diagram shown:

thalamus   hypothalamus   diencephalon   pituitary gland (aka hypophysis)

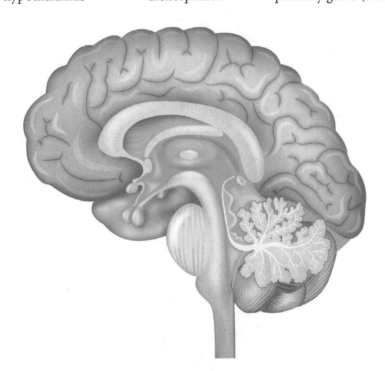

© Tefi/Shutterstock.com

DISSECTION OF A SHEEP BRAIN

In today's lab, we will be dissecting a sheep brain. The structures of this brain are nearly identical to a human brain.

PROCEDURE:
1. Obtain a pair of safety glasses. Make sure you clean them thoroughly.
2. Obtain a dissection tray, a scalpel, a probe, and a pair of gloves.
3. Obtain a specimen.
4. Observe the outside of the brain.
5. Remove any excess tissue that may be present.
6. Remove the dura mater, arachnoid mater, and pia mater.
7. Cut off about 1 inch of the spinal cord. Set it aside. You will observe this to answer the post lab questions.
8. Once you observe the outside of the brain and check off each of the features listed in the table below, cut the brain down the longitudinal fissure so that you have two halves. You will need to cut the cerebellum as well.
9. Identify each of the internal structures listed in the following table. Check them off as you find them.

Structure	✓
Dura mater	
Arachnoid mater	
Pia mater	
Cerebrum and cerebral cortex	
Longitudinal fissure and cerebral hemispheres	
Gyrus (singular) or gyri (plural)	
Sulcus (singular) or sulci (plural)	
Corpus callosum	
Lateral ventricles	
Thalamus	
Hypothalamus	
Pituitary gland (hypophysis)	
Pineal gland	
Third ventricle	
Pons	
Medulla oblongata	
Fourth ventricle	
Cerebral aqueduct	
Cerebellum	
Olfactory bulb	
Optic chiasm	

POST LAB QUESTIONS

1. How would you describe the dura mater?

2. Were you able to remove the pia mater? What was the degree of difficulty?

3. When you cut the cerebellum in half, you should have observed branches of white matter. What is the name of the white matter?

4. Draw the cross section of spinal cord (that you removed from your specimen) below:

5. What is the name of the hole that is present in the center? What is found inside this space?

UNDERSTANDING A REFLEX ARC

A reflex arc is a relatively rapid motor response to a stimulus. The spinal cord mediates and controls the response to a stimulus.

Let's pretend you are outside grilling on a beautiful summer day and you accidentally put your hand on the hot grill.

Using the diagram below, **identify and label each of the six components involved in a reflex arc**. When you are done with the diagram, **number the list in their correct order of occurrence**.

There are six components involved in a response:

_____ interneuron
_____ effector
_____ motor neuron
_____ receptor
_____ sensory neuron
_____ stimulus

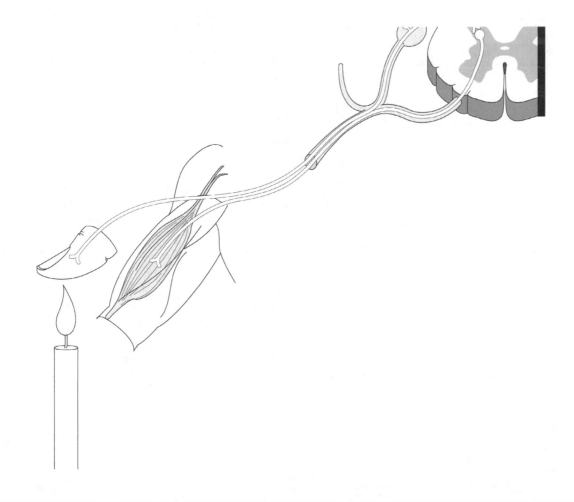

Illustration by Jamey Garbett © 2003 Mark Nielsen

DEMONSTRATION OF STRETCH REFLEXES

A reflex arc is the simplest type of nerve pathway that is a part of the nervous system. The pathway is in the following order:
1. receptor (receives a stimulus)
2. sensory neuron
3. interneuron
4. motor neuron
5. effector

There are two types of reflexes: a **stretch reflex**, which is a single synapse between a sensory and motor neuron in the gray matter of the spinal cord. An example of this is sometimes called a "knee-jerk" reaction—the movement of the leg after a strike to the patellar tendon. The second type is a **withdrawal reflex**, which also involves interneurons. An example of this would be withdrawing a body part away from something that is hot.

We are going to demonstrate **stretch reflexes** by tapping tendons. This will cause the muscle to stretch and initiate a movement.

PROCEDURE—REFLEXES:
1. Obtain a reflex hammer from the supply area.
2. Work with a partner to test each of the following reflexes.
3. Make sure your participant is completely relaxed or you won't be able to observe the correct response.
4. Complete the table with your observations.
5. Complete the post lab questions.

Reflex Tested	Instructions	Response Observed	Degree of Response (hypo-active, normal, hyperactive)
patellar	Gently strike the patellar tendon just below the patella.		
calcane-al	Gently strike the calcaneal tendon (aka Achille's tendon) just above the calcaneus.		
biceps	Place the arm so that the elbow is bent about 90 degrees. Press down on the tendon on the inside of the elbow. Gently strike your thumb.		
triceps	Have the participant lie on his/her back with an arm across the abdomen. The elbow should be bent about 90 degrees. Gently strike the triceps tendon just above the olecranon process.		
plantar	Have the participant take off a shoe and sock and run the handle of the reflex hammer across the sole of the foot. Start at the heel and move quickly to the big toe.		

Examiner: _____ Participant: _____

POST LAB QUESTIONS

1. What are stretch receptors? What is their scientific name?

2. Identify two more areas of the body that you would find these receptors.

Match each receptor type in column A with its description in column B.

Column A

A. nociceptors
B. Meissner's corpuscles
C. Pacinian corpuscles
D. thermoreceptors
E. chemoreceptors
F. baroreceptors
G. photoreceptors

Column B

_____ detects changes in chemical levels in the body
_____ detects temperature sensations
_____ detects changes in pressure in the organs of the body
_____ pain receptor; sometimes a free nerve ending
_____ detects deep pressure and vibration
_____ detects light for processing vision
_____ detects light touch

Answer the following questions.

1. What are the two types of pain?

2. How do general senses differ from special senses?

3. Describe the sympathetic nervous system. When is this system activated?

4. What are two other names for the sympathetic nervous system?

5. Describe the parasympathetic nervous system. When is this system activated?

6. What are two other names for the parasympathetic nervous system?

7. The vagus nerve is a cranial nerve but innervates more than just structures in the head region. What else does the vagus nerve control?

LAB: SOMATIC SENSES

General sense receptors are located all over the body and receptors are specific to each type of sensation. In this lab, we will demonstrate the sense of light touch.

PROCEDURE – PART 1:

1. Draw a 5 x 5 grid on the inside of your wrist. The grid should contain 25 little boxes and be about 2.5 cm wide by about 2.5 cm long. The grid should look something like this:

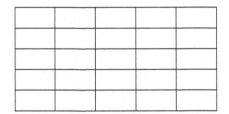

2. While you are looking away, have your partner use a small bristle to gently touch inside each of the squares. The partner should then record in each whether or not you felt the bristle.

3. Repeat steps 1 and 2, but this time the grid should be on the inside of your ankle.

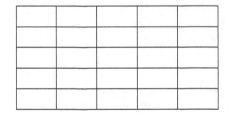

4. Repeat steps 1 and 2, but this time the grid should be on the outside of your forearm (opposite from the inside of the wrist).

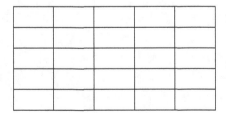

QUESTION

1. How would you describe the difference between the amount of light touch receptors from each of the areas?

PROCEDURE – PART 2:

1. Obtain a pair of calipers from the supply area.
2. With the tips of the calipers touching together, have your partner look away and gently touch each of the areas listed in the table below.
3. Record the number of tips distinctly felt when pressed against each of the areas.
4. Slowly spread the caliper tips apart in 1-mm increments until your partner can feel two distinct tips.
5. Record either a "1" or "2" in the data table below.

Region Tested	1-mm Distance	2-mm Distance	3-mm Distance	4-mm Distance	Final Distance for Two-Point Sensation
Forearm					
Leg					
Back of neck					
Back of hand					
Palm					
Fingertip					

QUESTION

1. Look over your data and determine which area(s) had the greatest capability to determine two points. Why do you think this is so?

Chapters 17-19 Lab

The Special Senses, The Endocrine System, and The Blood

CHAPTER 17 LAB

THE SPECIAL SENSES

OLFACTION

Olfaction is the scientific name for the sense of smell. Gustation is the scientific name for taste. Smell and taste go together. Receptors for smell are chemoreceptors and are located in the epithelium of the nose. For us to smell, the molecules of a particular odor must dissolve in the mucus and fluids present in the nose.

An interesting fact is that we have the ability to distinguish between about 10,000 different smells, and this is controlled by only about 1,000 different genes. Also, what is perceived as a particular smell by one person may be perceived quite differently by another person. This is another example of your brain making you unique.

Smell is something that we can adapt to very quickly. If we are exposed to a particular smell for a time, we no longer perceive it. If you have ever seen the commercial where a person becomes "nose blind," you can relate it to sensory adaptation.

PROCEDURE

Using the samples provided, try to determine the identity of each one. Record the results in the following table. The actual identity will be given at the end of the lab.

Sample #	Perceived Identity	Actual Identity	Sample #	Perceived Identity	Actual Identity
103			486		
111			515		
117			595		
123			620		
156			668		
201			695		
214			729		
256			765		
302			781		
344			804		
349			807		
362			822		
396			910		
410			942		
472					

On the diagram shown, label the regions corresponding to different taste sensations.

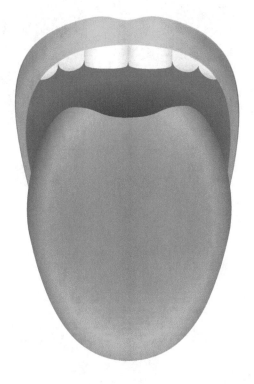

© Peter Hermes Furian/Shutterstock.com

1. Identify the cranial nerve(s) responsible for each of the following taste sensations:

Taste Sensation	Cranial Nerve(s)
sweet	
salty	
peppery/hot	
umami	
sour	
bitter	

2. About how many taste buds do we have on our tongue? _____

3. What are gustatory receptors? _____

4. What kind of muscle is the tongue? _____

5. Chemicals for taste must be dissolved in _____ to be perceived.

LAB: Identify the following parts of the eye and ear on models. Check off as you find them.

Eye Structure	✓	Eye Structure	✓
cornea		choroid	
sclera		retina	
iris		optic nerve	
lens		vitreous humor (area where found)	
aqueous humor (area where found)			

Ear Structure	✓	Ear Structure	✓
pinna/auricle		stapes	
tympanic membrane		cochlea	
external auditory canal		semicircular canals	
malleus		vestibule	
oval window		round window	
incus		Eustachian tube	
vestibulocochlear nerve			

1. Follow a light ray as it passes through the cornea to the retina. That is, list the structures in order beginning with the cornea and ending with the retina.

2. Follow sound waves as they enter the ear and leave through the round window.

EYE DISSECTION LAB

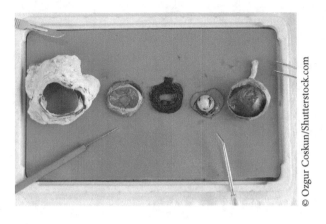
© Ozgur Coskun/Shutterstock.com

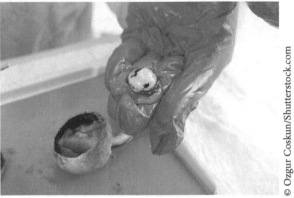
© Ozgur Coskun/Shutterstock.com

PROCEDURE:

1. Obtain a pair of safety glasses. Make sure to sanitize them before putting them on.
2. Obtain a dissecting tray, scalpel, pair of forces, a probe, and a pair of gloves.
3. Obtain an eye from the supply area.
4. Cut away all loose fat and other tissue from the eye.
5. Observe the outside of the eye.
6. Locate the optic nerve.
7. Cut the eye in half by making a circumferential cut around the eye. You should have a front and a back when you are finished. Be careful that you don't damage the internal structures of the eye.
8. Locate each of the structures in the following table. Check off each one as you locate it.

Structure	✓
sclera	
aqueous humor	
vitreous humor/body	
choroid	
tapetum fibrosum (the iridescent layer—found in animals to help them see at night)	
optic disc (this is the point where the optic nerve and the posterior wall of the eyeball meet)	
retina	
iris (notice the circular and radial muscles)	
pupil	
lens (cut this in half)	
cornea (this will appear opaque because the specimen has been preserved)	

POST LAB QUESTIONS

1. Which layer/tunic of the eye was the most difficult to cut?

2. What kind of tissue do you think is responsible for this quality of toughness?

3. How do you compare the shape of the pupil in the dissected eye with your own pupil?

4. Where was the aqueous humor in the dissected eye?

5. Describe the vitreous humor of the dissected eye.

6. Describe the degree of difficulty you had cutting the lens in half. Why do you think this is so?

7. What is the function of the circular muscle of the iris?

8. What is the function of the radial muscle of the iris?

IN-CLASS ASSESSMENT: Identify each of the structures presented on the screen.

The Eye: The Ear:

1. _____   1. _____

2. _____   2. _____

3. _____   3. _____

4. _____   4. _____

5. _____   5. _____

6. _____   6. _____

7. _____   7. _____

8. _____   8. _____

9. _____   9. _____

10. _____   10. _____

11. _____

1. How many of the eye structures did you correctly identify? _____

2. How many of the ear structures did you correctly identify? _____

3. How many of the total number of correctly identified structures did you absolutely know? _____
   __Guesses do not count!__

CHAPTER 18 LAB

THE ENDOCRINE SYSTEM

Place the following in the correct order for how a hormone is used.

_____ target cell   _____endocrine cell   _____bloodstream
_____ target receptor   _____hormone release   _____effector organ

Match each term in column A with its description in column B.

Column A
A. protein hormone
B. lipid hormone
C. prostaglandins
D. negative feedback
E. inhibiting hormone
F. releasing hormone
G. regulatory hormone
H. neural stimuli

Column B
_____ 1. coordinate local cellular activities; local hormones
_____ 2. hormone that binds to cell membrane receptor
_____ 3. hormone that stimulates secretion of hormones
_____ 4. hormone made of amino acids
_____ 5. uses a neurotransmitter at the endocrine gland
_____ 6. the main feedback control for hormone release
_____ 7. prevents secretion of hormones
_____ 8. hormone made of steroid

Complete the following questions.

1. List three general functions of the endocrine system.

2. Why are sweat, sebaceous, salivary, and mammary glands NOT part of the endocrine system?

3. Describe how a protein-type hormone affects a target cell.

4. Describe how a steroid-type hormone affects a target cell.

5. What is the role of the hypothalamus?

6. What is the role of the pituitary gland?

Label the glands of the endocrine system:

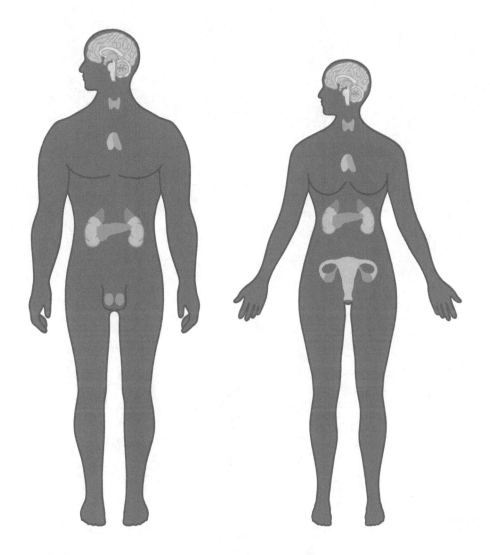

adrenal glands   pancreas   pituitary gland   pineal gland   thyroid gland
parathyroid glands   ovaries   testes   thymus gland   hypothalamus

Match the following glands to the hormones they secrete.

A	B	C	D	E	F
pituitary gland	thyroid gland	parathyroid glands	adrenal glands	pancreas	gonads

_____ epinephrine   _____ testosterone   _____ adrenocorticotropic hormone

_____ antidiuretic hormone   _____ glucagon   _____ luteinizing hormone

_____ thyroxine   _____ oxytocin   _____ parathyroid hormone

_____ growth hormone   _____ calcitonin   _____ thyroid stimulating hormone

_____ insulin   _____ estrogen   _____ aldosterone

_____ cortisol   _____ follicle stimulating hormone

_____ prolactin   _____ progesterone

Match each term in column A with its description in column B.

Column A

A. thyroid stimulating hormone
B. adrenocorticotropic hormone
C. follicle stimulating hormone
D. luteinizing hormone
E. prolactin
F. growth hormone
G. antidiuretic hormone
H. oxytocin
I. thyroxine
J. calcitonin
K. parathyroid hormone
L. cortisol
M. epinephrine
N. aldosterone
O. glucagon
P. insulin

Column B

_____ 1. water retention/conservation in the kidneys
_____ 2. stimulates the gonads to secrete androgens
_____ 3. stimulates muscle contraction of uterus and mammary
_____ 4. stimulates the adrenal cortex
_____ 5. used during immediate stress; full body response
_____ 6. stimulates the thyroid gland
_____ 7. stimulates calcium absorption in the bone
_____ 8. release glucose from liver during low blood sugar
_____ 9. used during long-term stress; prepares the body
_____ 10. stimulates the follicles of the ovaries
_____ 11. conserves sodium in the kidneys
_____ 12. increases metabolism throughout the body
_____ 13. removes glucose from blood when sugar levels are high
_____ 14. stimulates the mammary glands to produce milk
_____ 15. stimulates calcium release from the bone
_____ 16. stimulates growth processes throughout the body

Write the standard medical abbreviation next to each of the following hormones.

Hormone	Abbreviation
thyroid stimulating hormone	_____
follicle stimulating hormone	_____
antidiuretic hormone	_____
luteinizing hormone	_____
growth hormone	_____
prolactin	_____
thyroxine	_____
adrenocorticotropic hormone	_____
parathyroid hormone	_____

LAB: Identify the following endocrine organs on the models (torso, endocrine-plaque, and half-head). Check them off once you locate them.

Endocrine Organ	✔
hypothalamus	
pituitary	
thyroid	
parathyroid glands	
adrenal glands	
pancreas	
digestive tract (stomach and small intestine)	

Complete the following questions.

1. Explain the relationship between the hypothalamus and the pituitary gland.

2. What bone houses the pituitary gland?

3. Describe the negative feedback process (use TSH and thyroxine as an example).

4. Why are the adrenal glands called the "stress glands"?

5. Describe the function of prolactin and oxytocin with respect to the mammary glands.

HISTOLOGY OF THE ENDOCRINE SYSTEM

Sketch and label the representative portions of the following endocrine glands.

Pituitary Gland	**Thymus Gland**
Thyroid Gland	**Parathyroid Gland**
Adrenal Gland (medulla and cortex)	**Pancreas (exocrine and endocrine cells)**

THE BLOOD

BLOOD COMPONENTS AND FUNCTION

1. List the functions of blood.

2. Describe the basic function of each:

   a. red blood cells _____

   b. white blood cells _____

   c. platelets _____

LAB: **Use your textbook and/or blood poster to draw the following blood cell types.**

Red Blood Cell	Neutrophil	Eosinophil
◯	◯	◯

Basophil	Monocyte	Lymphocyte
◯	◯	◯

Match each term in column A with its description in column B.

Column A

A. hemoglobin
B. platelets
C. hemostasis
D. leukocytes
E. erythropoiesis
F. hematocrit
G. hypoxia
H. bone marrow
I. plasma
J. thrombin
K. blood typing
L. fibrin
M. erythrocytes
N. megakaryoctye

Column B

_____ 1. water and dissolved substances
_____ 2. low oxygen in blood
_____ 3. converts fibrinogen to fibrin
_____ 4. binds oxygen on red blood cells
_____ 5. the complex process of blood clotting
_____ 6. the term for making red blood cells
_____ 7. red blood cells
_____ 8. fragments of a cell; used for blood clotting
_____ 9. testing for the presence or absent of surface antigens on RBCs
_____ 10. will break up to make platelets
_____ 11. a diagnostic test that determines the amount of red blood cells
_____ 12. white blood cells
_____ 13. tissue that makes the blood cells
_____ 14. forms a net during blood clotting

1. Percent plasma in blood: _____

2. Percent water in plasma: _____

3. Percent formed elements in blood: _____

4. Percent red blood cells in the formed elements: _____

5. What are the three phases of *hemostasis*?

6. There are two types of blood clotting mechanisms. One is called ***intrinsic blood clotting*** and the other is called ***extrinsic blood clotting***. Describe each.

Answer the following questions related to blood.

1. What type of tissue is blood? _____

2. What determines the color of blood? _____

3. How much blood volume is inside you? _____

4. Nitrogen is found in the blood. What is its function? _____

5. What is the term for the production of erythrocytes? _____

6. What is the name of the protein that causes the production of erythrocytes? _____

7. What is the term for the process by which leukocytes leave the bloodstream?

   _____

8. What type of feedback controls blood clotting? _____

9. What is an abnormal blood clot called? _____

Read the following and place the steps of blood clotting in the correct order.

Let's suppose you are doing a documentary film to inform anatomy students about what happens when a blood vessel is injured. You will be able to shrink down and watch firsthand, from the inside, what happens inside of the body when a blood vessel is injured. Using the following descriptions of events, identify the correct order of what you will see when the body attempts to stop the bleeding.

A. Fibrin forms a network of threads.

B. Damaged tissues cause prothrombinase to be released.

C. Thrombin converts fibrinogen to fibrin.

D. The vessel is damaged and begins to contract.

E. A clot is formed.

F. Prothrombinase converts prothrombin to thrombin.

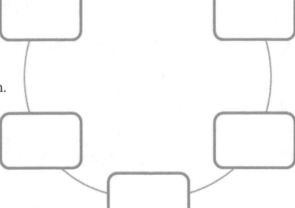

Start here

BLOOD TYPING LAB

OBJECTIVE:

In this experiment, the principles of ABO and Rh blood typing will be demonstrated by the method of agglutination (clumping). Four unknown samples of simulated blood will be supplied. The type and Rh are to be determined. The results are then to be correlated to the blood types of four imaginary people who are known to have each of the types of blood.

MATERIALS:

Blood typing plate
White sheet of paper
12 Toothpicks
3 Antisera (yellow, blue, and green capped)
4 Unknown samples of blood (red capped)

PROCEDURE:

1. Place the plate on a sheet of white paper. Shake each of the blood samples and the antisera to mix the contents.
2. Put 3 drops of unknown blood sample # 1 into each of the regions labeled A, B, and Rh on the plate.
3. Add 4 drops of the simulated anti-A serum (blue-capped) into the well labeled A onto the unknown blood.
4. Add 4 drops of the simulated anti-B serum (yellow-capped) into the well labeled B onto the unknown blood.
5. Add 4 drops of the simulated anti-Rh serum (green-capped) into the well labeled Rh onto the unknown blood.
6. Using a new toothpick for each well, mix the antiserum with the blood sample for 60 seconds. Do not use a toothpick on more than one sample. If a toothpick is reused, it will contaminate the second sample and the results for that sample will be incorrect.
7. Observe each mixture and record in the table that follows. If agglutination has occurred, use a + sign for agglutination; if no agglutination has occurred, use a – sign.
8. Repeat the steps for unknown blood samples #2, #3, and #4.

RESULTS

SAMPLE	ANTI-A	ANTI-B	ANTI-Rh	BLOOD TYPE	PERSON
1					
2					
3					
4					

INTERPRETATION

If a sample caused agglutination with the anti-A serum, it means that there was the A antigen attached to the surface of the blood cell. Similar reactions will be observed for the type B and Rh antigens. If both the anti-A and anti-B cause agglutination on a single slide, it means that both the A and B antigens were present on the blood cells. The following are the blood types of four imaginary people. Use this information to fill in the column labeled "Person" in the table on the previous page.

Person	Blood Type and Rh
Joe Schmoe	A+
Harry Hulk	B−
Jane Monroe	AB+
Lisa Williams	O−

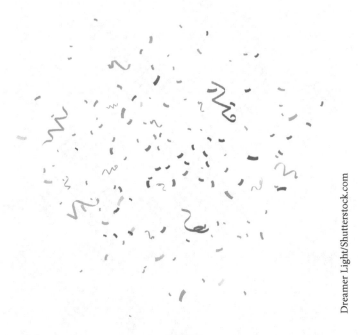

Dreamer Light/Shutterstock.com

YOU HAVE NOW COMPLETED THE WORKBOOK PAGES FOR A & P I! CONGRATULATE YOURSELF AND ENJOY YOUR SEMESTER BREAK! IT HAS BEEN MY PLEASURE TO HAVE YOU IN CLASS!